URTLE, CHELONIA MYDAS

ting beaches

rm, coldest month

37. Ulithi, Ifalik
38. Gaferut, Olimarao, Elato
39. Flying Foam Islands
40. Gulf of Carpentaria
41. Turtle Island
     (Great Barrier Reef)
42. Capricorn Reef
43. Kermadec Islands
44. Pearl and Hermes Reef
45. Lisianski Island
46. Laysan Island, Maro Reef
47. Laguna Ojo de Liebre
     (Scammon's Lagoon)

48. Bahía San Bartolomé
     (Turtle Bay)
49. Bahía San Ignacio
50. Bahía Magdalena
51. Gulf of California
52. Islas Tres Marías
     Cabo Corrientes
53. Michoacan Coast
54. Islas de Revillagigedo
     (Clarion, Socorro)
55. Cabo Blanco (Nicoya Peninsula)
56. Isla La Plata
57. Clipperton Island

The green turtle
and MAN

university of florida press
gainesville • florida • 1962

The green turtle
and MAN

by JAMES J. PARSONS

Members of the Caribbean Conservation Corporation inspecting a turtle at Tortuguero Beach. Left: Charles Bogert and Director James Oliver of the American Museum of Natural History. Center: Ben Phipps, President of the CCC. Right: Archie Carr.

A foreword
by Archie Carr

A geographer is a man to envy. Being by definition a student of the earth, he is free to go anywhere he can get a ticket to and tell of almost anything he can understand. When a geographer goes to a place like the Caribbean island of San Andrés, say, and comes away and writes about it, he doesn't have to stick to rocks, geckos, or folk songs as some specialists do. He can report on anything he wants to. One function of geography is to account for man as a feature of the landscape—and what is not grist for such a mill as that?

Well, James Parsons went to San Andrés, found it to be a charming island and wrote a solid geographer's piece about it. But this was not the whole outcome of his stay at San Andrés. Thinking back on what he had seen there, he focused on a single phase of Caribbean life that led into an extraordinary project. He set out to document the remarkable role in Caribbean and world affairs played by a single species of edible animal—the green turtle, Chelonia mydas.

The importance of the green turtle as a food resource in past centuries has been known for a long time. Bernard Lewis of Jamaica was the man who first got me excited about this, V with his clear and impressive essay, "Cayman Islands and Marine Turtle." The vicissitudes of turtling in the Cayman Islands are really the story of Chelonia in the western Caribbean as a whole. From Lewis' account, and from my own spot sampling of old records, I began to see that what had happened in the Caribbean was pretty much what had happened all over the tropical seas of the world. Until now, however, nobody has really brought in the material with which to reconstruct the primitive zoogeography of this extraordinary animal and to show its role in the furtherance of man's life and machinations in the tropics. That has been the aim and accomplishment of Parsons' book.

For a number of reasons the resources of the sea are hard to manage. Bodies of water can be more productive of food than land, and 70 per cent of the earth's surface is water. The potential food production of the sea is immense, and the actual harvested yield is a staggering figure. But so far the productivity of the sea is merely an expression of primeval bounty. At this stage of our understanding of the oceans, the only management practices possible are those that manage fishermen—that control the amount of the catch and the times of year at which it can be made. When people look at the mad spread of their species over the earth and shrug it off saying, why worry, the sea will feed us when we fill up the land, they may be right; but not necessarily so. Certainly not unless management of live marine resources can be made a lot more practicable than it is today. For the time being, the only beginnings of effective control have involved a few meek creatures of shore waters and estuaries. People seem to be doing pretty well in wheedling oysters into unnatural productivity, for instance; but for the foot-loose forms of ocean life management has hardly begun.

Three requisites for a valuable and controllable marine food resource suggest themselves: it ought to be big; it ought to be herbivorous, or at least close to the base industry in the feeding chain; and it has got to be edible. If we rule out the big plankton grazers like most whales and a few sharks, which strain their food out of the sea and so wander widely out of reach, two sets of creatures remain: the manatee-dugong group and the green turtle. At the present time we know too little about the natural history of manatees to say whether they might be tended up to feed our teeming descendants. With the green turtle they share the capacity to harvest marine spermatophyte plants—not just suck up drifting microscopic plankton, but gnash away at big rooted plants the size of parsley or Johnson grass, growing in steady spreads over

VI   endless miles of tropical ocean bottom. Today most of these *pastures are empty. There is good evidence that once they supported flotillas of green turtles. There is reason to believe that they can be made to do so again.*

There are still uncertainties in the planning for green-turtle management, but these do not concern the fundamental make-up of the food-chain involved, which is as clear and simple and direct as a steer in a field of alfalfa. It is just the sun, the green plant to catch up the energy of the sun, and the plant-eating animal to make steak out of the vegetation. The chain is short and uncomplicated and there is little chance of misfire along the line. In the case of the green-turtle chain, the only management required is making sure that a lot of turtles go on eating turtle grass. A new organization, The Caribbean Conservation Corporation, has recently grown up with this as its aim.

When Joshua B. Powers, an international publishers' representative in New York, read my book, THE WINDWARD ROAD, it suggested to him a way to carry out an old urge to help improve the lot of the people of the Caribbean littoral, where for complicated reasons protein hunger has been chronic for a long time and is getting worse as the population increases. Josh Powers organized the Brotherhood of the Green Turtle, a relaxed sort of society with no obligations for its members beyond thinking of ways to save the green turtle, and to set up a management program that might bring it back to primitive levels of abundance.

The restoration program took solid shape when John H. (Ben) Phipps, a philanthropist with a strong interest in zoology and wildlife conservation, decided that the green-turtle project seemed promising, gave his financial support to it, and became the president of its outgrowth, the Caribbean Conservation Corporation. During the 1961 season 18,500 baby turtles were produced at the organization's hatchery at Tortuguero, Costa Rica. The United States Navy sent down an amphibian airplane to distribute the crop among 17 different places about the Caribbean.

The main uncertainty in the outlook for managing Chelonia is its tendency to make long journeys between widely separated breeding and feeding places. With the support of the National Science Foundation we have for six years been trying to sort fact from fable in the body of rumor and folklore about the migratory feats of the green turtle. Returns from our tagging program have shown that the turtles are indeed migratory and that Tortuguero—Turtle Bogue, as it is known in Caribbean English—is the nesting center for green turtles from all corners of the western half of the Caribbean Sea. The spread between places in which tags have been recovered is nearly 2,000 miles. The pattern of the returns is strong evidence that the nesting schools that go to Tortuguero cross open water to get there.

This migratory habit complicates the outlook for culture and management because it takes the turtles periodically out of sight and into zones of uncontrollable factors. But the same habit makes the green turtle extraordinarily suitable for investigations in animal navigation. When the Tortuguero tagging results confirmed the widespread belief of fishermen that green turtles migrate, we looked about for a place in which to test the dimensions of the creature's navigation capacity. We found an ideal situation at Ascension Island, a volcanic crumb of land in the South Atlantic, halfway between Brazil and Africa. Turtles show up at Ascension each April to nest, and when they finish they disappear. Over along the Brazilian coast there are green turtles but no rookeries anywhere. So it seemed logical to suppose that Brazilian green turtles go all the way out to Ascension to nest. Tagging results confirmed this. If you look at a map you will see that making the 1400-mile journey from Brazil to Ascension on schedule is prima facie evidence of a very fancy guidance talent. So all at once the green turtle takes a place among the classic animal navigators, and while in some places it is being bred against future hungers, it is elsewhere being hung about with balloons and little radios in tests to track its courses in the open sea.

Because a green turtle takes half a dozen years to mature, it will be some time before we know how well the restoration program is working—whether the planted hatchlings stay at the places in which we want to re-establish nesting colonies, or are drawn instinctively back to the ancestral nesting site in Costa Rica when they reach sexual maturity. But meantime the new protection being given the Tortuguero rookery is each season sending extra swarms of baby turtles to increase the Caribbean fleets; and there has been a healthy awakening of interest in the project and in conservation generally among people who never thought of it before.

In this book Dr. Parsons has ransacked the archives to show the stature of the Homo-Chelonia relationship, to trace the history of this special case of man's exploitation of his environment. The book should have been written a long time ago. But because of the bivalent virtue of Chelonia—a guidance sense that may reach out to the stars, and its high promise as a means of raising the food yield of tropical seas—the need for the book has grown on apace during the years it was in preparation. It is sure to be welcomed by a great many people, with a great many different dreams.

Contents

A male green turtle. About the only time males are seen on land is when they are caught in the surf and stranded after chasing a female too close to shore. (CARR)

These modes, howe'er, are altered, and of late
Beef, but not Modesty, is out of date;
For now, instead of rich Sirloins, we see
Green calipash, and yellow calipee.

     —ROBERT MERRY, "The Dramatist" (1789)

The world's most valuable reptile

The edible green turtle (*Chelonia mydas*), renowned among mid-latitude epicures, is an important protein food resource for the inhabitants of many tropical coasts. In most of the world it is prized for its flesh, but in Southeast Asia the meat is seldom eaten and instead the eggs, which are systematically harvested, form a significant adjunct to the local dietary. During the breeding season the adult green turtles congregate in sometimes prodigious numbers off selected beaches, characteristically on sparsely peopled islands, where the females deposit their eggs at night in the warm sand. This extraordinary homing instinct, as much as its morphological characteristics, distinguishes the green from other marine turtles. Although normally confined to the warm seas (temperatures above 20° C. in the coldest month), it is occasionally carried into cooler waters by drift currents or storms (see front endleaf map). Stray greens have been reported off the coasts of England and of New England, as they have off Argentina and Chile.

1

The countless Turtle Islands, Islas Tortugas, Iles Tortues, and Schildpad Eilanden of the tropical seas bear witness to the remarkably localized nesting activities which have made the species uniquely vulnerable at the hands of man. Today, in several areas, the green turtle is in trouble, its range and numbers having been sharply reduced by the unrelenting demand of a burgeoning human population and the continuing activities of the turtle hunters. Professor Archie Carr has observed that, although the green turtle is the most valuable reptile in the world, it would be difficult to name any animal comparable at once in economic importance and in depletion of its numbers that is so poorly known (*33*).

Alone among the marine turtles, the green turtle is a vegetarian, browsing on any of the several marine grasses (e.g., *Zostera, Thalassia, Enhalus*) that grow along the shoal margins of tropical seas, and to this is sometimes attributed the superior delicacy of its flesh. A mature female turtle normally weighs approximately 250 pounds, but individual specimens weighing as much as 700 to 800 pounds were not infrequently reported in the past, especially among the Ascension Island and Seychelles aggregations. Immature "chicken-turtles" weighing 25 to 50 pounds, however, tend to be the most prized by gourmets for steaks, but they are said to be too "watery" for good soup.

Taxonomists are not yet agreed as to the extent and significance of the differentiation between the Atlantic-Caribbean breeding populations and those of the Indo-Pacific region. Carr, in his *Handbook of Turtles*, distinguishes the Atlantic green turtle (*Chelonia mydas mydas*) from the East Pacific variety (*C.m. agassizii*), at least on a statistical basis, by the brownish coloration of the carapace and leg skin of the former and a slightly different conformation of the shell (*32:345-65*). The predominantly greenish or olive-brown *Chelonia* of the western Pacific has been distinguished from either of these as *C. m. japonica*. However, the geographical races of the species have never been subjected to morphological diagnosis and their classification remains highly tentative. Interchange of Indian Ocean and South Atlantic turtles around the Cape of Good Hope has probably always been possible, but this clearly has not been the case as between the Atlantic and the eastern Pacific populations. Karl Schmidt has pointed out, however, that the extreme differentiation within this wide-ranging species should not be expected between the east and west coasts of Central America, which were connected by one or more straits through most of Tertiary time (*184*). The major faunal barrier, he suggests, was more likely the great stretch of open water in the eastern Pacific between Polynesia and the

American coast. Genetic isolation between the sea turtles on the east side of the Atlantic and those of the tropical western Atlantic is a further possibility, though a less likely one in view of the proximity of the west coast of Africa and the east coast of Brazil.

The habit of sun basking during daylight hours, reported from widely separated Pacific localities (Islas Revillagigedo, French Frigate Shoal, Galápagos, possibly Java), appears to be distinctive for this region, and there may be feeding and nesting traits as well that likewise distinguish one breeding aggregation from another.

These giant reptiles spend almost their entire life at sea, grazing on underwater pastures. Over most of their range only the adult female ever leaves the water and this she apparently does only at intervals of several years. Then, during the summer breeding season, she may lumber ashore during the night to deposit her clutch of 100 or more soft-shelled eggs the size of ping-pong balls in a hole she digs in the soft sand, her track, like a truck-tire tread, leaving telltale evidence to the egg hunters of her visit. This procedure is repeated four or five times at intervals of ten to fourteen days, while the males mill about in the water off-shore. Eggs laid at a given visit to a beach are not the ones fertilized at that time but are probably fertilized three years before, or at the last previous nesting-mating rendezvous (40). At the end of the breeding season the troop apparently returns to its feeding grounds, which may be, as with the Ascension Island turtles, as much as 1,000 miles away. These remarkable migrations must have been going on for a very long time. Hendrickson, who has published a comprehen-

Her eggs laid, a female green turtle, weeping and sighing, makes her laborious return to the sea.
(TOM HARRISSON, SARAWAK MUSEUM)

sive study of the ecology of the green turtles of the Sarawak Turtle Islands, suggests that the unerring pin-point accuracy of their homing pattern may be attributable to "experience-memory" related to particular beaches that are associated with "satisfactory" nesting experiences. Thus, new beaches might come into favor. He believes that the majority of stray *Chelonia* nesting on atypical beaches in Malaysian waters are smaller in size than the average adult female and suggests that these may be newly matured individuals (*106*:461-62). With the single exception of that at Tortuguero, on the Caribbean side of Costa Rica, where a mainland beach is backed by extensive swamps, the largest breeding concentrations that have been recorded are found on uninhabited or sparsely populated islands. The type of beach characteristically favored seems to be steeply sloping, with a beach platform high above the flood tide, and composed of a lightweight sand of medium coarse texture that does not pack easily into a hard surface.

During the breeding season the turtles are easy prey to harpoon or spear as they drift on the surface of the sea preoccupied in copulation. On their feeding grounds when they periodically rise for air they become readily entangled in giant drift nets set by the turtle hunters. Sometimes they are wrestled into boats by strong swimmers with the aid of a rope looped around one of the front flippers, or, even more remarkably, they may be brought to gaff by a remora, or suckerfish, tied to a long leash, that attaches itself stoutly to the carapace of the feeding turtle (see Chapter 3). A wooden decoy, carved in the crude form of a turtle, is frequently employed in American waters to lure the males, which may readily be harpooned or netted as they hopefully attempt to mount the deceitful temptress. In Fiji there are fanciful stories of "turtle callers," elderly women whose chants lure the turtles out of the sea. But these creatures, it is said, cannot be tricked by professional turtle hunters. Wherever the females go ashore to lay they may be rendered helpless simply by being "turned turtle" on their backs as they lumber across the sand to or from their nests, which are above high tide and generally at least 100 feet from the shore. The eggs, which have an incubation period of about 53 days, are very likely to be stolen either by man or beast. Finally, the newly hatched baby turtles, although they instinctively scamper in a beeline for the sea, must run a gauntlet of waiting predators, such as wild dogs, raccoons, giant crabs, barracudas, sharks, and oceanic birds, from which only a lucky few survive. Considering the towering odds against it, the wonder

is that the species has survived in such substantial, if dimin-

Mating green turtles thrown ashore by a breaker at Tortuguero Beach. (HIRTH.)

Anterior view of a Tortuguero green turtle laying her eggs. (CARR)

Ventral view of a male green turtle. Sometimes weighing as much as 800 pounds, green turtles are powerful swimmers but are completely helpless when flipped on their backs. (CARR)

ished, numbers. "To understand something of the size of the green turtle populations (of the Caribbean) under primitive conditions," writes Carr, "is to wonder how the species can exist at all today . . . with such markedly different levels of concentrations of individuals" (32:354).

The sighing of the captive turtle, left wheezing and immobile on its back, and the great tears that ooze from its big eyes have given rise to pathetic and exaggerated accounts of the animal's suffering. Yet even when the female hauls up on the beach to lay its eggs it weeps profusely and sighs—the tears perhaps nature's way of keeping sand from caking in its eyes as it excavates its nest, the sighs an admission that the buoyancy of the water is sorely missed by a 300-pound creature that is not structurally designed for life ashore.

The only other tropical sea turtle of commercial importance is the hawksbill or caret (*Eretmochelys imbricata*), whose mottled and translucent shell is the "tortoise shell" of commerce. The hawksbill has been intensively exploited at least since Roman times, especially in the Indian Ocean and the South China Sea, but recently the market for the shell, long used for furniture veneer and inlay work and in the manufacture of articles of feminine adornment, has been largely taken over by celluloid and plastic substitutes. The eggs of the hawksbill are equally as esteemed as those of the green turtle, but, as this species generally lacks the highly developed homing instinct of the latter, their collection on a large scale is impractical. Its flesh, while appreciated by some tropical dwellers, has not found acceptance among Europeans.

The other common marine turtles, the loggerhead (*Caretta* spp.), the ridley (*Lepidochelys* spp.), and the trunkback or leatherback (*Dermochelys* spp.) are generally considered inedible. As these, too, have a pan-tropic distribution there is a certain amount of inevitable confusion in identity as between them, the hawksbill, and the green. Moreover, long-distance or mass breeding is common to all five genera of sea turtle. But for the men who know turtles or know the sea there is generally no mistaking *Chelonia mydas* with its distinctive markings both on the shell and head, its white underside or plastron, its social nesting habits, and, above all, its highly palatable flesh.

CULTURAL ATTITUDES TOWARD THE MEAT AND EGGS

The green turtle is exploited alone for its edible properties, its shell being considered worthless. The first Europeans who encountered it in the tropical seas thought of it chiefly as providing an antidote to scurvy and an *elixir vitae* of extraordinary virtues. Later, especially in the West Indies, its flesh became a staple for both whites and slaves, either salted and buccaned or fresh. Baked turtle, the flesh often minced fine and cooked in its own shell, early became a plantation-house delicacy. Turtle oil, from any of several species, was used as a substitute for butter, as a lamp fuel, and as a lubricant.

By the mid-eighteenth-century a trade in live turtles had begun to develop between the West Indies and London, where green turtle and green-turtle soup were coming to have a prestige value among the well-to-do. "A plate of turtle, green and glutinous," the flavor and consistency of good veal, increasingly provided the *pièce de résistance* of diplomatic dinners and ceremonial banquets. The cartilaginous greenish substance that lines the shell, both the light-colored "calipee" and the darker "calipash," gave the soup the cherished gelatinous consistency. It was employed as part of the stock (this being made from the whole turtle, less the guts) and also was cut into small chunks and added as a garnish to each portion. Calipee and calipash are the unossified parts of the bellyplate and backbone. The calipash is widest in young turtles, for as they age the backbone extends to the edge of the shell. But the thickening with age of this layer of soft stuff tends to compensate for this change. Calipee, more abundant than calipash, is concentrated along the mid-strip of the bellyplate. The term "calipee," apparently of West Indian origin, was at first applied to the belly, or underside, of the turtle while the "calipash" was the upper side or carapace. By the nineteenth century these terms had come to be applied specifically to the delicately flavored gelatinous substance that comprises much of the lower and upper shells. On the Great Barrier Reef of Australia, however, it is otherwise. There "calipash" refers to the flesh attached to the lower shield and "calipee" to that obtained from the flippers, but this is contrary to the usage elsewhere (*153*:112). In preparing calipee and calipash for shipment, the shell was first cut into strips and boiled for several hours, after which the gelatinous matter was severed from the bony plate and dried in the sun. These stone-hard strips, looking like pieces of dried glue, have been exported under the name of "turtle strips," "calipee," or, less properly, "turtle fat" to mid-latitude markets for at least a century and a half. A large turtle may produce two and a half to three and a half pounds of it, the flesh being wasted if there is no local demand or refrigeration facilities.

As a symbol of Victorian opulence turtle soup was especially esteemed by nineteenth-century English and American aristocrats, a cherished luxury especially associated with the Lord Mayor's and aldermen's banquets. For the initiated it stood almost in a class by itself, like oysters, "to be approached with diffidence and reverence." While its prestige today is much reduced, there is still a substantial market for clear green-turtle soup among epicures. This, coupled with a growing demand for meat within the tropics, has led the few biologists who have studied it to express concern for the future of the species.

The sea turtle is sacred or held in special veneration by many peoples. In early China both the land tortoise and the sea turtle were symbolic of the good life and the long life and have always had a certain religious significance. Edward H. Shafer, of the Department of Oriental Languages of the University of California at Berkeley, informs me that the earliest Chinese literature is full of enthusiastic reports about the eating qualities of turtles. Most of these were apparently fresh-water species, but one ancient book, full of the South, the *Ch'u tz'u*, refers to the "broth of the sea turtle." We cannot be sure what species was used. The pharmacologists often recommended turtle broths and soups for their excellent tonic properties. The green turtle seems to have been less well known to the Chinese than the hawksbill. The early name of the former was *kou-pi*, a word that is unidentified in modern dictionaries of Chinese. Today it is referred to as *lü tzu-hsi*, "green sea turtle." Its flesh seems to have been especially prized. A commercial product called "*[kou-]pi* skin," which was submitted as tribute to the T'ang court by the city of Canton, could only have been calipee (*186*). It was described as being "extremely rich and savory." There is a ninth-century reference (*Ling piao lu i*) to sea turtles being common off the Kwantung coast; men could ride on their backs. There is also reference to a "kou-pi islet" on the way to Liu-ch'iu (Formosa?). The green turtle is said still to nest occasionally on some of the small islands south of Hong Kong (*108*).

Both in Asia and in the Americas the turtle was one of the mythical animals on which the world was believed to rest. The Burmese are said to consider sea turtles divine, keeping them in tanks in pagoda grounds where they are fed special foods. Among the north Australian aborigines the sea turtle is one of the principal totems. Pliny wrote of a cave-dwelling people at the entrance to the Red Sea who, although they were *Chelonophages* ("turtle eaters"), worshipped the turtle as sacred. Among many groups extraordinary medicinal virtues are attributed to the oil of turtle. It is perhaps not surprising, then, that the eating of turtle flesh is taboo among

8

several peoples and of ceremonial significance among others. For example, the flesh of sea turtles seems not to be consumed by most Burmese, Thai, or Malays. In its stead these people have traditionally and intensively exploited the nearby turtle islands for the eggs, seemingly with little impact on the size of the permanent populations. Hendrickson has suggested that the concentration on egg collecting and the consequent protection of living turtles as providers of eggs have been more effective means of species conservation than the more common prohibition against the taking of eggs (106:525). This proposition seems to be borne out in the survey of the world's green-turtle nesting beaches in the pages that follow. On the turtle beaches that have had their stock most reduced, meat not eggs has been the principal object of exploitation.

In Southeast Asia the avoidance of sea-turtle flesh is sometimes held to be a Muslim trait. For example, Thomas Forrest, in Indonesian waters nearly 200 years ago, wrote that "some of my people, who were not Muslims and eat turtle, cut the meat up small and stewed it in green bamboos" (71:126). However, it does not appear to be followed by the Muslim population of East Africa and Arabia. There appears to be nothing in the Koran that specifically forbids the eating of sea turtles. Moreover, the avoidance of sea-turtle flesh, though apparently not tortoise flesh, seems to be as characteristic of most coastal peoples of Burma and Thailand as of the Malays, suggesting that it may well be a pre-Muslim attitude of considerable geographic extent. Hendrickson is of this opinion (106:457-58). According to Theobald, "land and freshwater testudinata are a favorite article of food of all classes in Burma, save such as have embraced Islam, or Jews." But marine turtles, he noted, were generally not molested except for their eggs (203:8). Tandy also notes that land and river tortoises are valued by the Burmese for both flesh and eggs, but he makes no mention of sea turtles (202:155). Among the modern Thai the eating of turtle is considered unthinkable, although they may eat poultry, pork, and beef with relish. But this taboo seems not to extend to India. Paul Wheatley has pointed out to me that turtle and tortoise flesh were both being served at banquets in royal courts in the Kelantan Valley, Malaya, early in the seventh century, where the rituals, pageantry, and protocol were of Hindu character.

In China and India, as well as among Southeast Asia's Chinese and Indian populations and the Hindu-influenced Balinese, turtle flesh is highly regarded. Field biologists in Malaya and Sarawak, on the other hand, have found that popular attitudes against killing of adult animals are so

9

strong as to make it impossible to study food habits or intesti-
nal parasites of turtles or to carry out other projects which
demand the sacrifice and dissection of the creatures. This
avoidance of turtle flesh most often seems to stem from the
peculiarly high esteem in which sea turtles are held in this
part of the world. Thus, in the Maldive Archipelago, where
sea turtles abound, J. Stanley Gardiner reports that they are
not eaten because the natives believe "they suckled Kom-
burani when he hauled up the islands from the deep with
his fish-hook" (75:2:1050). François Pyrard, more than 200
years earlier than Gardiner, had noted that turtle flesh was
taboo among Maldivians "because, they say, this animal has
some kind of conformity and kinship with man" (171:80:348-
49).

Some native American groups seem likewise to have avoided
turtle meat, perhaps in a sort of subconscious recognition of
the species' vulnerability to man. Rochefort, for example,
clearly stated that the Caribs of the Lesser Antilles originally
did not eat turtle meat, being fearful of taking on the characteristics of that reptile (179:2:202-3). Yet they relished the
eggs. On the west coast of Central America, and in Brazil
too, some early accounts suggest that eggs or oil, rather than
meat, were the primary interest of at least some aboriginal
10   groups.

In Africa similar avoidance patterns probably existed. On the east coast, for example, the Cushite peoples of Somaliland are still today said to disdain sea-turtle flesh (95:126). In Mauritania, according to Villiers, it is especially the food of the lower classes (224:93). The Imragen Moors of Arguin in Mauritania were described by Valentín Fernandes in the sixteenth century as living largely on sea turtles (224:76).

The Europeans who first came into contact with the green turtle were not of one accord in their judgments of it. Some asserted it to be a delicious and healthful food, while others held that it was poisonous. It was generally the English who were most enthusiastic in their praise of the green turtle's virtues, perhaps because they knew it best. As a cure for scurvy and a relief from the monotony of a hardtack and salt beef diet it was much prized by the early explorers and buccaneers. George Woodbury suggests that the green turtle as much as any other natural factor was responsible for the opening up of the Caribbean and the concentration of piratical activities in that part of the world (237:106-10; see also 33:17). The great clumsy creatures were easy to catch, abundant, nourishing, and most important of all in the tropics before refrigeration, could be kept alive for weeks. William Dampier, that rough seaman who, Oliver Goldsmith observed, had added more to natural history than half of the philosophers who went before him, made repeated and extensive reference to turtles in his *Voyages,* written between 1681 and 1688. To men of his ilk the facts of green-turtle geography were of prime significance. He was the first to make clear the distinction between the edible green turtle and the other, less palatable species, especially the hawksbill and the loggerhead.

The health-giving qualities of *Chelonia mydas* were much commented on by observers of the seventeenth and eighteenth centuries. John Fryer, to whom it was "neither fish nor fowl nor good red herring," observed that "it restores vigor to the body, giving it a grace and luster as elegant as viper wine does consumptive persons and worn out prostitutes" (73:306). Indeed, many an ill-disposed Englishman on Jamaica went to the Cayman Islands during the turtling season to recover his health feasting on turtle (53:2:399). Syphilitic patients are said to have been sent to the Cape Verde Islands from Portugal for the same purpose (190:225). Both flesh and eggs were reported to be slightly aphrodisiac, and still are considered so among some peoples.

Turtle was in as great demand as a slave food in the West Indian colonies in the seventeenth and eighteenth centuries as was salt cod from Newfoundland. Gradually the reptile was

11

taken up by the West Indian white aristocracy. It was considered a special delicacy when eaten fresh. "To eat this animal in the highest perfection," wrote Oliver Goldsmith, "instead of bringing the turtle to the epicure, he ought to be transported to the turtle" (82:674). Janet Schaw, writing of her visit to Antigua in 1774-76, said, "I have now seen turtle almost every day, and tho I never could eat it at home, am vastly fond of it here, where it is indeed a very different thing. You get nothing but old ones there [London], the 'chickens' being unable to stand the voyage; and even these are starved, or at best fed on coarse and improper food. Here they are young, tender, fresh from the water, where they feed as delicately and are as great epicures as those who feed on them.... Could an alderman of true taste conceive the difference between [turtle soup] here and in the city, he would make the voyage on purpose, and I fancy ... into the other world before he left the table" (183:95).

The special quality of turtle soup was said to be that it did not "cloy." In other words, one could eat almost any quantity of it without ill effects. Its easily assimilated proteins, without carbohydrate or fat, were said to prepare the stomach in superb fashion for what was to come. When banquets started with this soup, the diner was considered best able to enjoy the numerous rich dishes to follow. Goldsmith wrote that turtle "has become a favorite food of those who are desirous of eating a great deal without surfeiting . . . by the importation of it alive among us, gluttony is freed from one of its greatest restraints" (82:674). The soup, flavored with sherry, capsicums, ginger, cloves, and nutmegs, and served piping hot, was considered at its fiery best "when, after having eaten, one is obliged to rest with his mouth wide open, and cool the fevered palate with Madeira or Port" (189:366). In twenty years in the West Indies, one doctor professed, he had never heard of an "accident" arising from eating it! It was also held to be an ideal food for convalescents, especially when served in jellied form.

The Dutch, although they partook of it, seem to have been rather indifferent to turtle, in the East perhaps because of their close association with the Malays, who avoided the meat. The French, although interested, found but a limited supply of green turtle (tortue franche) available to them, most of the best turtling grounds being under English control. From the seventeenth-century account of Père Labat, the Dominican monk, of the many ways of preparing turtle that he observed in the manor houses of Martinique and Guadeloupe, it is evident that its merit was not unrecognized (125:1:61-62, 137-38). Yet it did not rate so much as a mention in Brillat-

Savarin's exhaustive *Physiologie du goût,* written in 1825. That the French thought of it as an English dish is suggested by the account of it in the nineteenth-century Larousse dictionary. "Like all people, says Grimod de la Raynière, the English possess some national ragouts which they esteem more through the spirit of patriotism than through conviction and the French, lovers of novelty and ever ready to judge their neighbor's possessions above their own, have the kindness to envy them. Such is turtle soup" (*128*:324). While he considered the reputation of English turtle soup fully justified, the French cuisine critic Alfred Suzanne wrote in 1904 that the green fat was esteemed by London connoisseurs more for its rarity than for its taste. As for the meat, he judged it a little dry, sometimes having a slightly disagreeable fishy flavor. In France, he noted, turtle soup was still scarcely known but by name, while in England and America it had an enormous consumption (*201*:12).

In contrast to the north Europeans, both the Spaniards and the Portuguese were for the most part singularly disinterested in turtle. After the middle of the sixteenth century their chronicles are generally silent regarding its occurrence and use. Sometimes there is evidence of a positive prejudice against eating the flesh, perhaps a reflection of native Indian attitudes which they encountered on the mainland. It is noteworthy that the English in the Antilles were not generally in direct contact with Indian populations, while on the mainland the Miskitos of Central America, their principal associates, were extraordinarily avid turtlers and turtle eaters.

Cadamosto, the first Portuguese to mention what must have been the green turtle, fed it to his crew at the Cape Verde Islands in 1456 and found it palatable (*30*:65). Oviedo, in his *Historia Natural,* called it "good and healthful food" (*163*:111). Indeed, prior to the arrival in force of the English, the Spaniards seem to have had considerable respect for green-turtle meat as a food. In his late sixteenth-century account of Cuba, Fray Alonso Ponce (*169b*:2:373) remarks on the many small boats that came to the port of Havana loaded with large turtles that had been harpooned off the coast. They were kept in staked pens in the harbor to await buyers. Thomas Gage, the English Jesuit, who was in the New World from 1625 to 1637, observed of Havana that "all ships make their provision for Spain of tortoise meat [there]. They cut the tortoises in long thin slices . . . and dry it in the wind after they have well salted it, and so it serveth the mariners in all their voyages to Spain, and they boiled it with a little garlic, and I have heard them say that to them it tasted as well as any veal" (*206a*:334). Elsewhere he wrote of his voyage to America: "We fed for the first week [in the West Indies] upon almost nothing but tortoise. . . . Our Spaniards made with them an excellent broth with all sorts of spices. . . . Thus, our hens, our sheep, and our powdered beef, and gammons of bacon, which we brought from Spain, were some days slighted, while with greedy stomachs we fell hard on our sea veal" (206a:28). Clearly, the Spaniards' prejudice against turtle meat that was later so evident had not yet taken hold. Most Spanish and Portuguese writers, however, ignored it.

Dampier, describing the turtles found on the Brazilian coast, wrote in 1699: "neither the Spaniards nor Portuguese lov(e) them; Nay they have a great antipathy against them, and would rather eat a porpoise, tho' our English count the green turtle very extraordinary food. The reason that is commonly given in the West Indies for the Spaniards not caring to eat them is the fear they have lest, being usually foul-bodied, and many of them pox'd (lying as they do so promiscuously with their Negrines and other She-slaves) they should break out loathsomely like lepers; which this sort of food, 'tis said, does much incline men to do, searching the body and driving out any such gross humours" (53:2:399). Richard Walter, who was with Lord Anson on his voyage around the world, writing in 1748, thought it strange, considering the scarcity of provisions on the Pacific Coast of Central America, "that a species of food so very palatable and salubrious as turtle should be proscribed by the Spaniards as unwholesome and little less than poisonous. Perhaps the strange appearance of this animal may have been the foundation of this ridiculous and superstitious aversion, which is strongly rooted in all of the inhabitants of this coast." Of the Indians and Negroes, slaves of the Spaniards, that they had taken as prizes in Peru, he noted: "These poor people being possessed with the prejudices of the country they came from, were astonished at our feeding on turtle and seemed fully persuaded that it would soon destroy us . . . it was with great reluctance and very sparingly that they first began to eat it; but the relish improving upon them by degrees, they at last grew extremely fond of it, and preferred it to every other kind of food . . . a food more luxurious to the palate than any their haughty Lords and Masters could indulge in . . ." (226:208).

One may ask, of course, whether the Spaniards' apparent disinterest in turtle may not have been in part a reaction to the close identification of it with the rival and hated English. Frederick Simoons, in his study of Old World food prejudices, has shown the frequency with which particular animals or foods have become identified with particular ethnic, religious, or other groups through the course of history. The tendency to identify peoples with distinctive food habits is only a step from the rejection of foods simply because they are associated with a rival group. The pastoralists' rejection of the pig, an animal closely associated with and symbolic of the settled farmer, seems to be an extreme, but by no means isolated, example of this sort of attitude (*191*:106-25).

Even today the turtle is relatively little exploited among the descendants of the Spaniards and Portuguese in tropical America. The commercial turtlers in the Caribbean are for the most part English-speaking whites from the Cayman Islands, while the principal local markets for turtle meat are in the Negroid mainland towns such as Colón, Limón, Bluefields, and Belize where English-speaking Protestants of West Indian ancestry predominate (*165*).

THE EPICURES AND THE TURTLE TRADE

Although the virtues of turtle had long been familiar to West Indian planters and to men of the sea, its introduction onto the tables of London seems to have been curiously delayed. In Lyttelton's *Dialogues of the Dead* there is one between Apicius and Darteneuf in which the latter, who died in 1738, is made to lament that turtle was not known in his lifetime (quoted in *157*:12:168-69). The *Gentleman's Magazine* in 1753 and 1754 carried several notices of large sea turtles, brought from Ascension Island and the West Indies, being dressed at public houses in London. One of the turtles, "a present to the gentlemen of White's Chocolate House," was brought by Lord Anson. At the Kings Arms tavern in Pall Mall the mouth of the oven had to be taken down to admit the plastron of another 350-pound specimen. "It may be noted," one of the notes observed, "that what is common in the West Indies is a luxury here" (*77*:23:441, 498; 24:337).

Although these were certainly not the first live green turtles seen in England, they were a sufficient rarity to gain newspaper comment. "Of all the improvements in the modern kitchen," said the *World* in an account of a City of London banquet about this time, "there are none that can bear a comparison with the introduction of the turtle" (quoted in *157*:9: 114-15). Dr. Samuel Johnson, in his *Dictionary* (1775), tersely defined "turtle" as a term "used among sailors and gluttons for a tortoise."

As the English demand increased, vessels in the West Indian trade were provided with flat wooden tanks in which live turtles could be deck-loaded. Although they were fed grass 15 and banana leaves on the journey, after arrival at the Leadenhall Street turtle tanks they still had to be "brought into flesh before being dished up to aldermen's or noblemen's tables." The largest, which were not necessarily the best, were often destined for the royal palace. For the less affluent there already were substitutes. As early as 1808 Mrs. Raffald's *Experienced English Housekeeper* was offering a recipe for "artificial" or mock turtle made from a calf's head (*174*:82-83).

Shipping losses of live greens may have been heavy. Peter Simmonds thought that "the best way to send home turtle from Ascension is to head them up in a sealed cask and have the water changed daily by the bung hole and a cork. Turtle, though the extremes of heat and cold are equally injurious to them, should always arrive in hot weather in England. Thus, an unfortunate captain on one occasion took from Ascension 200 turtles and, timing his arrival badly, brought only four alive to Bristol" (*188*:180).

Steam communication greatly facilitated the movement of live turtles across the Atlantic. By 1878 the annual arrivals were said to have reached 15,000, most of them caught by the Cayman turtle fleet and forwarded through Jamaica (*189*:364-65). Their weights ranged from 25 to 300 pounds and their aggregate value in that year was estimated to exceed 8,000 pounds sterling. "The locality for feasting on turtle," it was written, "now has been transferred chiefly to the precincts of the City; and the Ship and Turtle, Birch's in Cornhill, the Guildhall, and Mansion House are the chief depots of consumption" (*77*:23:441).

Imports of "preserved turtle" were initiated in 1841 from Jamaica. It was admitted duty free as "fish of British taking and imported in British ships" after the entrepreneur, Henry Gunther of Kingston, assured the Commission of Privy Council for Trade that the turtles had been taken by Cayman Islanders and, thus, by British subjects (*85*). By 1880 imports of "prepared turtle" were listed as 10,800 pounds (*190*:226). This was apparently the designation applied to the sun-dried meat and calipee that in late years had begun to place turtle soup, by one account, "within the reach of the general consumer." But it was to remain pre-eminently a prestige food. Mrs. Beeton called turtle soup "the most expensive soup brought to the table," one guinea being the standard price for a quart of it. The 1909 edition of her widely read *Book of Household Management* states, "The price of live turtle ranges from 8*d.* to 2*s.* per pound, according to supply and demand. When live turtle is dear, many cooks use the tinned turtle, which is killed when caught, preserved by being put into hermetically sealed cannisters, and so sent over to England. The cost of a tin, containing two quarts or four pounds is about £1, and for a small one, containing the green fat, 3s. 6d. From these about six quarts of good soup can be made. Sun-dried turtle is also sold, and answers very well. It requires to be soaked, as well as stewed for a long time, and put into good stock" (14:178-80).

The question of what makes a proper stock for turtle soup had been debated in a series of letters to the editor of the London *Times* that appeared in that paper between November 13 and 16, 1883. The claim of Sir Henry Thompson that conger eel made the best and most widely used stock and that "turtle furnishes only the garnish and the name" was vehemently refuted by the proprietors of Painter's Ship and Turtle on Leadenhall Street: "We never use or have used conger eel or stock meat of any kind; the stock is from turtles themselves, of which we kill from 4 to 8 daily. In proof of above, kindly test soup sent herewith ... and you will find it, as we guarantee, perfectly pure turtle."

Painter's was unique of its genre. "Turtle soup from Painter's in Leadenhall Street," wrote one observer at the end of the last century, "is decidedly the best thing in the shape of soup that can be had in this, or perhaps any other country." Here, it was asserted, was the only "turtle artist" in Europe (104:124-25). A French visitor described the establishment in 1904. A large pool of water contained upwards of fifty turtles awaiting "sacrifice." Alongside was the slaughter room and next to it the kitchen, where ten to twelve men were occupied in making this national soup, which was sent out each day to the city, to the provinces, and even to foreign markets. It brought the exorbitant price of one guinea a liter for the regular soup and twenty-five shillings for the clear soup. A bowl of turtle soup served in the restaurant cost three shillings, including the glass of punch that followed it (201:15).

Blending and seasoning are of the greatest importance in soup making and they call for much experience and "know-how." Like the proprietors of the Ship and Turtle, some leading present-day processors of "the Queen of Soups," such as Lusty's of London and Moore & Company of Newark, New Jersey, insist that the fins and steak or inside red muscle meat of the turtle are chiefly responsible for the flavor and that genuine "real turtle soup" of the sort that jells of its own strength on cooling is properly made only from a broth of turtle meat to which diced calipee is usually added as a relish. Others, especially in London and on the Continent, regard beef stock as an essential basis of the soup, holding that without it turtle soup tends to lack character. In this they claim the support of the famous *maître chef* Escoffier. The

17

so-called "mock turtle" soup generally contains no turtle whatever, calf's heads being used to simulate the gelatinous consistency of turtle soup. In the United States and Great Britain mock turtle is usually a thick soup, but on the Continent it is also prepared clear. Where the more expensive calipee is used in place of calf's heads, the soup may be designated as "real turtle soup," although properly speaking it is not such. The demand for calipee is strong and apparently growing, suggesting its increased use as an additive to soups of other stocks.

Tinned turtle products first entered mid-latitude markets sometime about the middle of the nineteenth century. Some of the first canneries were located within the tropics, close to sources of supply. A Key West factory was reported turning out 200,000 cases a year in 1880, employing ten vessels and sixty men in gathering the turtle (190:226). Another early one was at Pearl Lagoon, Nicaragua (51:274-76). The "green fat," a membrane lining the inner shell, formerly in strong demand, was often tinned separately from the meat and soup. It was once customary to serve it as a side dish, a spoonful being added to the soup if desired, but today there is no market for it. The largest shipments of tinned turtle products were to London, but New York was a substantial secondary market. Although turtle canneries have operated from time to time in Jamaica, Nicaragua, Grand Cayman, Mexico, Australia, North Borneo, and Kenya, they have been for the most part short-lived ventures. Today the larger share of the green-turtle soup and meat that goes into cans is processed either in the New York area or in London.

The leading London soup maker, John Lusty, Ltd., "By Appointment Purveyors of Real Turtle Soup to the Royal Household since the Reign of Edward VII," has been in business since at least 1851, when John Lusty was registered as a Marine Stores and Turtle Dealer at the Parnham Street address, close by the London docks and Greenwich Naval Base, where the company remains today.* Captains of the Royal Navy ships returning from the West Indies or Ascension Island often brought back live green turtles that they wished to be made into soup for presentation to "My Lords of the Admiralty," who prized it as a great delicacy. Trading vessels also brought their quota of the giant reptiles. The tinning of turtle products was initiated by Lusty's in 1870, with the West Indies as the principal source of supply. In a special

* I am grateful to Ralph Lusty of John Lusty, Ltd., for these notes on the history and present activities of his company. E. M. Hodgkinson and Samuel L. Yates of the United States Embassy in London have also been helpful.

Labels from cans of green-turtle soup and meat, produced chiefly for a gourmet clientele, suggest the diversity of this modern industry in both Europe and America.

heated indoor pool, with a sandy beach, the turtles lived a life of ease until required for the soup pots. Since World War II, however, very few live turtles have been imported, as shipping lines no longer provide deck facilities for them. Today they are usually slaughtered at the port of shipment, degutted and refrigerated. Lusty's imports perhaps 600 frozen carcasses annually, mostly from Kenya, and about 20 tons a year of Seychelles dried calipee and dried flipper and neck meat. Most of the latter is sold to others, for Lusty's gets most of its requirements from the whole carcasses it uses.

The real turtle soup, such as is served in the City of London at the Lord Mayor's banquet and similar sumptuous affairs, is a rich, gelatinous, clear soup that will set in a natural jelly even before it is completely cold and will almost "stick the lips together" when eaten. The preparation of this specialty product, in 200-gallon units, takes four to five days and requires about 2,000 pounds of turtle, the equivalent of perhaps 10 carcasses. A long, slow cook is essential to get the full benefit of the turtle and to ensure proper blending of the vegetables, herbs, spices, and wine. Before being put into cans, it is clarified. On custom orders, delivered in large crocks as a stiff gelatin, extra spice and wine are often added.

Lusty's, like other importers, also supplies fresh turtle meat

19

to caterers, hotels, and steamship companies for special banquets. Although the company makes several specialty soups, turtle products account for the largest part of its business. These include several types of soup, a meat extract, tinned turtle steaks in Madeira sauce, tinned calipee, a cosmetic oil for soap and face cream, and even a stick shaving soap with a turtle-oil base.

The second major London producer of real turtle soup is Bender & Cassel, Ltd., who also market bird's-nest, shark's-fin, kangaroo-tail, and other specialty soups under the trade name "Becas." Production began in 1936. Company officials state that they import "a few hundred turtle carcasses and several tons of sun-dried calipee and calipash" each year. Most of the carcasses are from Jamaica, where turtles taken by Caymanian schooners are slaughtered and quick-frozen. The dried calipee and calipash comes both from Grand Cayman and from the Seychelles.

One recent trade estimate suggests that 1,200 frozen green-turtle carcasses may enter the London market in a year. Beach-turned females are avoided because of their generally poor condition. Most of the imports are from East Africa. On the average they run much larger than those that had earlier been brought from the West Indies, where offerings have recently dropped off sharply. Dried calipee, which in 1960 was bringing eighteen shillings ($2.25) a pound for the better quality grades of lighter color, is as important to the soup makers as are the whole carcasses. It is estimated that 30 tons of it may cross the London docks in a year, but this figure probably includes some dried meat as well as calipee destined for re-export to the Continent.

In late years a substantial demand has developed for green-turtle soup in several countries on the Continent. It is a standard feature of the menus of many luxury restaurants and hotels, particularly in the larger cities and tourist centers of Germany, the Low Countries, and, to a lesser extent, of France. In addition to imports from Great Britain there is a considerable domestic production. In Western Germany Eugen Lacroix of Frankfurt-am-Main and H. W. Appel Feinkost of Hannover are probably the principal factors in the trade, in France Edouard Artzner of Strasbourg and Conserves Morvandelles of Autun. Turtle soup is also canned in Denmark and in Switzerland. For most of these concerns the Indian Ocean is the principal source of supply, both for dried and frozen turtle meat. Increasing amounts of the finished products have recently been exported, especially to America. The Lacroix company, which has been manufacturing turtle soup since 1921, claims to use some 150 tons of cut turtle

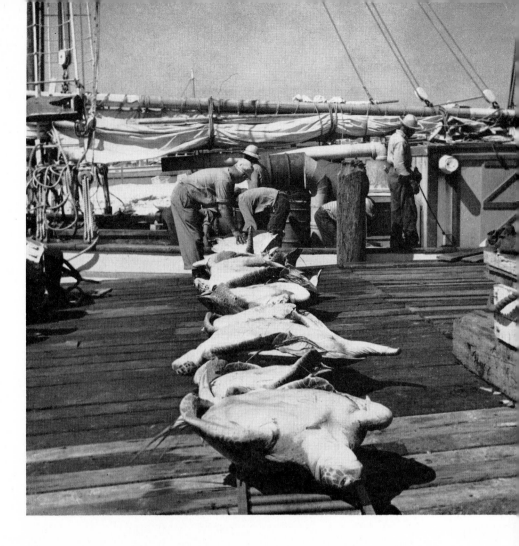

Unloading green turtles from the Miskito Coast of Nicaragua at Key West, Florida, for transshipment to New York.

(FLORIDA STATE NEWS BUREAU)

meat and turtle carcasses annually and also claims that its product is the world's "most bought" turtle soup. But the latter claim is disputed, both in Britain and America.

In the United States the dominant company in the green-turtle and turtle-soup business is Moore & Company Soups, Inc., of Newark, New Jersey ("Ancora" brand).* The company has been making turtle soup since 1883. Formerly the turtles arrived at the port of New York deck-loaded on banana boats, but today they are trucked from Tampa, Key West, and other Florida ports turned on their backs, flippers tied, and heads supported by wooden blocks to minimize the danger of deaths from road jars. An average of two truck loads a week are received at the Newark plant, where they are held in a pond until slaughtered or, if frozen carcasses, placed in refrigerators. The tendency here is to use more red

* Andrew Perelli, vice-president of Moore & Company Soups, Inc., has provided much of the information that follows. This concern was formerly located on Manhattan Island. It moved to New Jersey following World War II because of increased requirements for space.

21

meat and less calipee ("shell meat") than in former days. Major hotels and restaurants may either buy direct from Florida dealers or from Moore's. As supplies are irregular and a few dealers tend to monopolize the trade, Moore & Company maintains working arrangements with Florida buyers and even some of the Cayman turtle-boat captains.

Turtle flesh apparently finds special favor among the Chinese population of New York. On August 24, 1939, the *New York Times*, describing the escape of a large sea turtle from the Fulton Street fish market, quoted an observer to the effect that 80 per cent of the turtles brought to the market were consumed by Chinese, "who believe that they acquire the turtle's longevity by eating its flesh."

During World War II frozen green-turtle steak, unrationed, was said to have been especially in demand in New York, where it replaced higher priced and hard-to-get beef. It was sold without bones for 75 to 80 cents a pound, and can still be obtained today in certain butcher shops there, as well as in many southern cities. However, the greater share of it undoubtedly goes to the canners.

Published trade statistics for 1957 list imports of 1,033,187 pounds of live turtles into the United States for that year, more than four fifths of which were from Nicaraguan and Mexican waters. No figure is given for calipee. If the average weight of the individual turtles was 160 pounds, this would mean that approximately 4,000 animals were imported, and this would not include any landings from United States vessels working in Florida waters nor any imports of calipee. While this figure would seem to be substantially in excess of the annual imports into European markets, it must be recalled that dried meat and calipee plays a much greater role there than in the American industry. Imports into the United States in 1960 were less than half as much as in 1957.

One may hazard the guess that between 15,000 and 20,000 green turtles a year find their way, in one form or another, to the commercial markets of North America and Europe, but this would include the animals slaughtered at Seychelles and elsewhere exclusively for their calipee and calipash. Although the aristocracy may consume less turtle soup today than in times past, the market has been immensely broadened. What was once reserved for the epicures of London and New York is now available on the shelves of quality groceries throughout Europe and America. The implications of such an expanding demand in the mid-latitudes, coupled with the growing population of the tropical world, are regarded as ominous by marine biologists and other persons concerned with the preservation of the species.

22

The beach at Talang Talang Besar, Sarawak, where up to a million green-turtle eggs may be collected in one season.
(TOM HARRISSON, SARAWAK MUSEUM)

Historical survey of the principal turtling grounds

The history of commercial turtling probably begins in the Bermudas. This isolated mid-Atlantic island group, originally an important nesting and feeding area for *Chelonia mydas*, lay conveniently athwart the sailing route between the West Indies and Europe. As early as 1594 there is an account of a shipwrecked crew using turtle oil to caulk a leaky vessel and later taking on thirteen live turtles for the continuation of their voyage to Newfoundland (76). In 1609 there are reports of "a great store" of greens there, yielding an oil "as sweet as any butter ... one of them sufficing 50 men a meal." Two boats could take forty in a day. Wanton destruction of this fortuitously located meat reserve, both by harpooning and by turning the females on their backs as they came ashore to lay, followed permanent English settlement in 1612. In 1620 the

NOTE: The front endleaf map shows the location of the principal nesting beaches and feeding grounds mentioned in the text.

24   Bermuda Assembly, concerned with "the danger of an utter de-stroyinge and losse of . . . so excellente a fishe," passed what must have been one of the New World's first conservation meas-ures (32:355). It prohibited the killing of turtles less than eighteen inches long within five leagues of the land. The pen-alty was to be forfeiture of fifteen pounds of tobacco. As turtles became scarce in local waters, Bermuda turtle boats moved fur-ther to sea in pursuit of them; toward the end of the eighteenth century they are reported in the Bahamas and at Ascension Island (233:374).

Today, though a few stray turtles may nest on the more remote islands of the Bermudas, they are essentially tourist curiosities (9: see also 149). Babcock's account tells us that in 1937 there were still two turtling boats operating during the summer months where at the turn of the century there had been eight. The record catch of one of the captains, who had been turtling for forty years, was seventeen in one week and sixty in one season. The supply was inadequate to meet local demand, as it still must be, so that live turtles were being imported from the West Indies. Bermuda turtlers, hurt by high wage rates, were requesting a protective tariff! The organized turtle industry has since ceased to exist. Large turtles are no longer caught in Bermuda waters, fifty pounds being close to the average weight. These represent an itinerant popula-tion of juveniles, without eggs, and may be presumed to be flotsam that has drifted with the Gulf Stream the 800 miles from the Bahamas or the Greater Antilles. In the past, indeed, regular migrations between the Bahamas and Bermuda seem a distinct possibility.

Although the Bahamas are recorded from earliest times as supporting a large population of browsing greens, attracted by the extensive local eel-grass flats, there seems to be no evi-dence that they ever bred there. Mark Catesby asserted cate-gorically that they did not, although hawksbills, logger-heads, and leatherbacks all nested on Bahaman beaches. All of the greens taken in his day were harpooned while feeding, the Carolinas providing the principal market (41:2: 38). The name of Green Turtle Cay, off Eleuthera Island in the Bahamas, might be taken as suggestive of at least one local-ized nesting beach, but there is no information as to how or when it was named.

The pressure on the Bahaman green turtles was sufficient that as early as 1671 the Lord Proprietors of Carolina asked Bahaman officials to prepare a bill to be presented to Parlia-ment "for the preservation of turtle" (86:7:No. 712). Appar-ently this instruction was not immediately carried out, for it was repeated five years later. As late as 1878 green turtles were being sent in small numbers from Turks Island to New York markets. They seem always to have been taken in nets, usually set at the mouths of the salt-water "creeks" so common in the Bahamas (*134*:83). Boats from the Bahamas participated in the decimation of the Florida east coast and Cuban grazing flats and of the breeding school that came each year to the Dry Tortugas (*33*). The remnant Bahaman turtle population today is small and dispersed, being of no commercial importance, and the meat and eggs of other varieties are more commonly available than those of the green turtle.

John Hawkins, who called at the Dry Tortugas in July, 1563, was perhaps the first Englishman to eat turtle meat in the New World. He found it "much like veal," although the eggs he found in those turned on the beach "did not eat very swelly" (*103*:46-47). The Dry Tortugas may well have been the source of supply, too, of some of the Spanish trading sloops, laden with "hides and live turtles," that the Dutch buccaneers captured off the north coast of Cuba, near Havana, in the early years of the seventeenth century (*127*:34:45; 35:41). When Audubon was there 300 years later, turtles were still apparently abundant, perhaps more of them loggerheads than greens. He heard a report while there of one man who had harpooned 800 greens in a single month in adjacent waters, but was unable to verify it (*5*:2:371-80). Today this once populous nesting ground is rarely if ever visited by green turtles.

Carr believes that the Dry Tortugas beaches were once the main source of supply for Florida waters and that since their exhaustion the origin and thus the character of the remaining Florida population has changed accordingly (*37*:6-7). He estimates that as many as 1,000 green turtles may be taken annu-

Three turtles taken at the seasonal turtle fishery off the Florida west coast. Turtle at lower left is about average size for the Florida population. That above is a 340-pound male, and the biggest taken in 20 years. The big-headed turtle at lower right is the mysterious ridley, whose breeding place until recently has been completely unknown. (CARR)

Docking a green turtle at Yankee-town, Florida. A small green-turtle industry still operates off the west coast of Florida, where each season several hundred turtles are taken between Tarpon Springs and the Apalachicola delta. Arriving in April and disappearing in November, they obviously come from distant breeding grounds—possibly in Costa Rica. (CARR)

ally in Florida waters, mostly in the grass flats off the Cedar Keys, on the Gulf side, but they are nonbreeding juveniles, probably waifs and strays from the main Caribbean population. Green turtle nestings on the Florida mainland are today quite rare. The Key West turtle trade, the town's most active industry in the 1890's, now depends largely on imports from Mexican and Central American turtling grounds. Shrimp, not turtles or sponges, dominate the Key West economy, although at least one concern still cans green-turtle soup and prepares fresh turtle meat for northern markets (215:513-15).

In earlier times the green turtle must have played an important role in the economy of coastal Florida. William Tecumseh Sherman, who was stationed at Fort Pierce, on the east coast, in 1840, wrote: "They are so cheap and common that the soldiers regarded it as an imposition when compelled to eat green turtle steaks instead of poor Florida beef or the usual mess-pork. I do not recall in my whole experience a spot on earth where fish, oysters, and green turtle so abound as at Fort Pierce, Florida" (187:19 quoted in 39:316). Green turtles are today rarely seen in the waters north of Florida, yet F. W. True wrote in 1884 that they were plentiful as far north as North Carolina where one man could catch 100 off Cape Hatteras in one day, apparently immature specimens carried by the northward-trending Gulf Stream (quoted in 32:347). Loggerhead and leatherback turtles still make their nests in some numbers on the coasts of Florida and Georgia.

26

THE CAYMAN ISLANDS, MISKITO COAST, TORTUGUERO AND YUCATAN

Of all the *Chelonia mydas* nesting beaches that the Europeans found in the American tropics none compared with the Cayman Islands. For nearly 200 years ships of all nations resorted there each summer to turn green turtles and to dry their flesh, an easily obtainable and palatable protein for ship or plantation stores. The Caymans early came to be the center of the Caribbean turtle industry, and the English from Jamaica, who first settled on the islands in the 1660's, came to be renowned as skilled turtlers. Although the greens no longer nest on the Caymans, nor are taken in local waters, the Cayman-based turtling fleet, operating off the Central American coast some 350 miles from Grand Cayman, still supplies the largest share of turtles entering foreign markets from the Caribbean. There can be few finer examples of cultural conservatism and persistence in the New World than that of this isolated island community of seamen.

It was Columbus himself, in 1503 on his fourth voyage, who first observed the massing of turtles at the Caymans. His brother Ferdinand wrote of the occasion, "on Wednesday May

27

10 we raised two very small and low islands full of turtles, as was all the sea about, so that they looked like rocks; whence these islands were called Las Tortugas" (quoted in *148*:636). The reference was to Little Cayman and Cayman Brac, about 115 miles northwest of Jamaica and 40 miles east of Grand Cayman. No stop was made.

The turtles congregated there especially during the summer months. Those who later touched at the islands at other seasons of the year were impressed rather by what were taken to be giant *iguanas*, alligators, and crocodiles that also lounged on the shore and from whence the name "Caymans" (Spanish, *caimanes*) began to appear on the charts. But it was the abundance of green turtles that brought men back. The Dutch chronicler Johannes de Laet, recounting the journey of Pieter Adriaensz Ita in July, 1630, describes one sandy beach on the northwest corner of Little Cayman "where from May to October great numbers of edible turtles come to lay their eggs in the sand . . . [so that] in a single night one or two thousand can be taken, and of such a size that 20 to 30 men can be fed with one of them" (*127*:35:170). Two thousand turtles in a single night is a quite incredible number—perhaps the author meant two hundred—but granting the exaggeration, it suggests that the nesting turtles may have been no less common on the beaches of Little Cayman than on Grand Cayman in those early years. But the latter probably persisted longer as a major supply source, the "meat market" of the English and Dutch in the Caribbean. William Jackson, who was on Grand Cayman in 1643, wrote "Hither doe infinnit numbers of sea tortoises resorte to lay their eggs upon ye sandy bay, which at this time [June] swarm so thick. The island is much frequented by English, Dutch and French ships, that are purposely there to salt up ye flesh of these tortoises" (quoted in *63*:15).

"Making turtle at Caimanos" was a frequent log-book entry of vessels operating in this part of the Caribbean in the seventeenth century. A Captain James is recorded as landing 50,603 pounds of salt turtle at Jamaica in the summer of 1657, valued at 3*d.* a pound. Another 43,000 pounds, brought by the same skipper two years later, was sent on to Barbados (*86*:9:Addenda 290, 316).

There were some forty sloops based at Port Royal turning turtle at the Caymans and netting them in adjacent Cuban waters when Hans Sloane wrote (ca. 1688). He observed that the meat "sustains a great many, especially of the poorer sort" on Jamaica, the live turtles being "put into pens or palisadoed places in the harbor of Port Royal" to await slaughter (*193*:1:xvii). The great Palisadoes sandspit that encloses

Kingston Harbor and on which Jamaica's international airport is built was named for these turtle pens or "palisadoes."

When French and Spanish corsairs drove the English turtle sloops from the Caymans and the south coast of Cuba in 1684, Jamaican officials considered it as a calamity. Colonel Hender Molesworth wrote to William Flathwayt in London: "The turtling trade being thus lost for awhile, Port Royal will suffer greatly. It is what masters of ships feed their men on in this port and ... nearly 2,000 people feed on it daily here, to say nothing of what is sent inland.... It cannot easily be imagined how prejudicial is the interruption of the turtle trade. We must inevitably set ourselves to remove the existing instructions." To this end he asked for more armed frigates "if our Lords think that our turtlers and traders should be protected" (86:11:721).

Dampier, who was at the Caymans in 1675, observed that there were no feeding flats in the vicinity of the islands and surmised that the breeding turtles must come from the south keys of Cuba, forty leagues away. "And it is most certain," he wrote, "that there could not live so many there as come here in one season" (53:1:133; 2:399). Edward Long, in 1774, commented in wonderment at this annual migration, which he thought originated in the Gulf of Honduras: "without the aid of chart or compass [they] perform this tedious navigation with an accuracy superior to the best efforts of human skill; insomuch that it is affirmed that vessels, which have lost their latitude in hazy weather, have steered entirely by the noise which these creatures create in swimming, to attain the Caymana isles. . . . In these annual peregrinations across the ocean they resemble the herring shoals; which by an equally providential agency, are guided every year to the European seas. . . . The shore of the Caymanas, being very low and sandy, is perfectly well adapted to receive and hatch their eggs; and the rich submarine pastures around the larger islands afford a sufficient plenty of nourishing herbage, to repair the waste which they have necessarily undergone. Thus the inhabitants of these islands are, by the gracious dispensation of the Almighty, benefited in their turn; so that when the fruits of the earth are deficient, an ample sustenance may still be drawn from this never failing resource of turtle, or their eggs, conducted annually as it were into their very hands" (136 quoted in 32:350-51).

Subjected to such sustained slaughter, the Cayman breeding population was doomed to extinction. By 1802 the islands were reported as contributing but a small part of the turtles that were being taken by Caymanian turtlers (132). Gradually the turtle boats had turned to other waters, first to the

Cuban keys and, when they too were swept clean, to the Gulf of Honduras and the Miskito Coast of Central America. By 1722 several "Jamaica vessels," some of which were possibly of Cayman origin, were annually visiting these waters to catch turtle and to buy them, together with tortoise shell, from the Miskito Indians (68:9:155). Dried manatee meat was also supplied to English traders for export to Jamaica. A few years later the British superintendent of the Miskito Shore establishment observed that the salt flesh of turtle from the Miskito Cays sold in Jamaica at the price of salt beef and was much esteemed. Three men and a boy might get 130 in a season, each yielding some 150 pounds of dressed meat.

The Miskito Indians may well have taught the English the art of turtling. As early as 1633 a trading station had been established among the Miskitos at Cape Gracias a Dios by English adventurers from the Puritan colony at Old Providence Island, some 160 miles to the southeast. From the beginning relations between native and trader had been amicable, and a sort of symbiotic relationship soon grew up, nurtured in part by a mutual antagonism towards the Spaniard, that survived for better than two centuries (166:10 ff). The Indians were not only superlative boatsmen but they had an "eye" for turtles that never ceased to amaze the Europeans. Many an English and Dutch pirate vessel carried at least one Miskitoman as a "striker" to harpoon turtle or fish for the mess table. Dampier is again our principal authority: "Their chiefest employment in their own country is to strike fish, turtle and manatee . . . for this they are esteemed and coveted by all privateers; for one or two of them in a ship will maintain 100 men, so that when we careen our ships we choose commonly such places where there is plenty of turtle or manatee for these Moskito men to strike; and it is very rare to find privateers destitute of one or more of them when the commander or most of the men are English; but they do not love the French, and the Spaniards they hate mortally" (53:1:39).

The first clear documentation of the presence of Caymanian turtlers at the Miskito Cays is in 1837, the year after the Cayman colony was established at Roatán in the Bay Islands of Honduras (63:165; 132:56-65). Thomas Young, writing in 1842, noted that Cape Gracias a Dios was "often visited by small schooners from Grand Cayman's Island, near Jamaica, to fish for turtle near the Mosquito Keys, about 40 or 50 miles from the Cape, and which seldom return without a rich harvest. They supply the Belice and Jamaica markets with the finest green turtle, and often . . . hawksbill turtle shell, as the Mosquito Keys are very much the resort of that species as well as the green" (238:17). Cayman boats also visited Roncador and the other uninhabited low reefs between Jamaica and Old Providence Island, but there they took chiefly hawksbills.

In the National Archives in Washington (*Miscellaneous Letters Relating to the Guano Islands,* Vol. 5) there is a contract dated September, 1869, between James W. Jennett of Brooklyn, New York, and two natives of Martinique whom he had left at Roncador to sell guano to passing ships and to await his return. He instructed them to catch and save all the green and hawksbill turtles they could and to build a turtle crawl with stone to keep them in. One dollar in gold was to be paid for each green turtle weighing above 75 pounds, one cent per pound for the smaller ones and for all hawksbills.

Every year during the season from ten to twelve vessels of Cayman registry still are to be found netting turtles at the Miskito Cays (166:33-37). (These Cayman vessels were more numerous in earlier years. A Bluefields newspaper reported twenty-three of them present during the summer of 1905, each taking 100 to 200 turtles. The Nicaraguan government objected at that time to their violation of the three-mile limit.) They pay Nicaraguan customs officials at Cape Gracias a Dios a nominal fee for each of the 2,000 to 3,000 green turtles annually taken under terms of a treaty of 1916 between the United Kingdom and Nicaragua. The turtle ground is a vast sandy shoal covered with marine grass and set with scattered coral rocks. Working from small catboats, the turtlers set their nets over marked rocks to which the turtles customarily retire at night and wait for them to become entangled in the nets when they surface to blow. The night's catch from each catboat is transferred to a larger schooner and on Saturday the week's turtles are taken to the "crawls" at a temporary camp on one of the cays where fresh water can be had. Archie Carr describes this turtling (33; see also 205:13-17). Some turtles may be slaughtered and the meat sun-dried on the cays, but the majority are carried live, at the end of the season, to Grand Cayman where they may be kept in crawls for several weeks before marketing. It is apparently here that they lose much of the sea lice that gives them their somewhat unattractive appearance. Caymanian exports of green turtles in 1956 were 4,109 live animals valued at £20,000 sterling, together with 24,000 pounds of "turtle skin" (calipee) worth £18,000 sterling f.o.b. (92).

The inhabitants of tiny Cayman Brac have been traditionally the hawksbill fishermen, while those of Grand Cayman have confined their attentions to the green variety. Cayman Brac inhabitants are even said to prefer the flesh of the hawksbill to that of the green. Their method of capturing turtles is quite different, involving a "turtle trap" consisting of an iron ring about five feet in diameter to which a simple net bag is attached. The turtle is stalked in clear water and, when sighted, the net is dropped over it. But synthetic plastic products have brought about what is almost certainly the permanent collapse of the market for tortoise shell, and the great piles of shell stocked here, some of it now more than twenty years old, will probably never find a buyer. In their economic distress the people of Cayman Brac have turned in recent years to handicrafts, especially rope products, but not to green turtles (63:25, 359-60, 428).

Grand Cayman turtle boats can reach the turtling grounds off Nicaragua in three or four days. When the Nicaraguan government has from time to time challenged the legality of their presence off the Miskito Cays, they have shifted to Mexican waters or to Costa Rica. Traditionally there have been two turtle fishing seasons, one from January to March or April, the other from July to September. Spring and early summer, the months of roughest water, are thus avoided. But the second season of calms is also the season of hurricanes and through the years these tropical storms have taken a heavy toll of Cayman turtlers.

Briefly, in 1952, a turtle-soup cannery was in production on Grand Cayman, built and operated by the Colonial Development Corporation. The anticipated American market failed to develop and the enterprise was closed down at the end of the year after 22,000 dozen cans (8,600 cases) of soup had been produced. The 30,000-case annual capacity of the plant was never realized and the Corporation investment of £70,000 was written off as a loss when the cannery closed in May, 1953, "owing to sales failure." The report for 1953 bluntly concludes: "The Corporation should not have embarked on the production of an article of such limited luxury interest on its own. Negotiations for the disposal of the factory by lease or sale are proceeding. Under the existing agreement turtles will be taken from the fishermen's association up to June 30, 1954, and sold live in the U.S.A." (*213*:1952:34; 1953:29). So ended the Grand Cayman turtle cannery scheme.

The green turtle seldom nests on the Miskito Coast today. Yet it once may have done so. Mr. David Stoddard informs me that he has seen in the Belize Archives a proclamation dated at Bluefields July 26, 1844, prohibiting "the thoughtless and improvident practice of destroying the nests of turtles for the purpose of carrying off their eggs." This prohibition applied to the nests of all species of turtles on any portion of the Miskito Coast, its islands, keys, and shoals.

32

Tagging a large green turtle at Tortuguero. (CARR)

The local belief that they come from Tortuguero (Turtle Bogue), a twenty-mile stretch of black sand beach lying between Río Tortuguero and Río Parismina in Costa Rica, is being borne out by the tagging program being carried out by Archie Carr (38).* Tortuguero, indeed, appears to be the last large-scale nesting area for the Atlantic green turtle in American waters. Each summer huge fleets of turtles appear there, mate off the shore, and (the females) lay their eggs on the beach. This part of the coast, lying immediately south of the Río San Juan, has been known as a favored area for turtles since at least 1592, when there is a Dutch account telling of the great numbers that came to lay in the sand there "much as crocodiles do" (135:92). Their flesh, the chronicler tells us, was very good. Today it is leased in ten-mile sections to contractors for turtle-turning and egg-gathering. During the season, from June 15 to August 15, about 2,000 female turtles averaging 250 pounds each are turned by the concessionaires. By law this may be done only after the eggs have been laid, but the *veladores* ("stayers-awake") who patrol the beach each night are paid by the head for all turtles turned and are unsupervised. Taken to Limón, the turtles are placed in crawls and fed on bananas and banana leaves until sold, usually for about ten United States dollars each. The best export market is Colón, the mature females turned on the beaches being larger and less esteemed, as well as more difficult to handle, than the 100- to 150-pound specimens taken by the Cayman boats off the Miskito Cays. The English-speaking Negroes ("Creoles") of

* See back endleaf for tag recoveries in migration study.   33

Central America are especially fond of the meat, which normally sells at a slightly lower price than beef on the local markets. A few are shipped to Key West and other Florida ports, though not so many as in former years when banana boats carried turtle tanks on their decks.

According to one of the concessionaires, at least three times as many turtles could be taken from Tortuguero if the market warranted it. He estimates that more than three fourths of all eggs laid are lost to predators, especially dogs, and that more than 80 per cent of all baby turtles actually hatched are taken by sharks or other fish as they enter the sea. There are few historical records of the exploitation of Tortuguero. In 1923 the United States Consul at Limón estimated the annual take to be only 750 greens a year and an equal number of hawksbills. The greens sold for about $10.00 apiece, about the same as today (*212*:598-99).

Although there seems to have been no diminution in the turtle catch from Central American waters and beaches in the past fifty years, the meat-hungry settlements along the coast and the new quick-freeze storage techniques may be building up a pressure that the species will be in no position to withstand. Carr, who initiated a tagging program at Tortuguero in 1955, has emphasized the urgency of basic research in the biology of the animals, their range, breeding habits, nesting places, migrations and volume of the annual take of turtles and eggs throughout their habitat area (*32*:356-57). Such information would provide data on which a proper conservation program could be founded, and green turtles could perhaps be restored to their former abundance. A recent survey supported by the Caribbean Commission concludes that the principal danger to the industry as a whole is interference with the nesting turtle and that prohibition of egg taking and capture of turtles on beaches should be rigidly enforced (*115*:59-61).

There is another nesting area off the Yucatán peninsula of Mexico, second in importance only to Tortuguero, which Carr surmises may be the home of the remnant Florida west coast grazing population. This is centered on the low coral islands off the northeast corner of the peninsula, especially Isla Contoy, Isla Blanca, Isla Cancún, and the uninhabited eastern coast of the larger island of Cozumel. Green turtles are also reported to nest in considerable numbers on Banco Chinchorro (Cayo Lobos) off southern Quintana Roo. The headquarters for commercial turtlers here is Isla Mujeres, itself a raised limestone block with a cliffed coast on all but its northern tip. Although unpopulated for most of its history, Isla Mujeres is today the site of a lighthouse and small fishing community.

Exports of green turtles to the United States from this part of the Mexican coast have numbered as high as 2,000 a year, but in the summer of 1956 it was being claimed that taxes and export duties were making the trade uneconomical. At that time there were several hundred turtles in the crawls at Isla Mujeres for which it was said that no market could be found. (This information is from Señor Hilario Scumperdis, Isla Mujeres; on this turtlery documentation is scarce, but see 199:2:355-59, 384, 411, and 65:90-92).

The turtles of the Mexican coast had early come to the attention of the Spaniards. Juan de Grijalva's expedition of 1519 encountered Indians carrying turtle-shell shields which sparkled so in the sun that some of the soldiers contended that they were made of low-grade gold (61:49). At a somewhat later date (1554) the natives of at least one coastal village on the Bay of Campeche (Amescalapán, near Coatzacoalcos) were ordered to pay a tribute of five *tortugas* every two months, along with substantial amounts of cacao, maize, and cotton cloth (145:19). What the Spaniards may have done with these turtles is not known. They may have been hawksbills, but the use of the term *tortuga* rather than *caret* on the tribute list argues rather for the green variety. In either event the seasonal nature of their migrations does not seem to have been recognized. A few years later the village in question was reported abandoned (*despoblado*).

The green turtles that were formerly so plentiful among the cays of British Honduras may well have come from the Mexican beaches. An English logwood buyer, Nathaniel Uring, who was at Belize in 1719, observed that "Among the small islands or keys of the Bay are great numbers of green turtles, which the Baymen never want when they fish for 'em, and are mostly taken in nets." These must have been feeding turtles, although when he was at Isla Carmén on Laguna de Términos, Bay of Campeche, in July seven years earlier, he mentioned that two of his men in one night turned ten "fine, large turtle . . . on which all the ship's company feasted . . . it being that time of year when those creatures go on shore to lay their eggs" (217:166, 243). It was the custom of the Jamaica logwood cutters at Campeche and Belize to keep a reserve supply of live turtles in pens or crawls, and many of these found their way to the Jamaica market, where they were especially in demand as food for plantation slaves.

THE LESSER ANTILLES, THE GUIANA COAST, ALTA VELA, AND ISLA AVES

In the Lesser Antilles and along the north coast of South America green turtles seem originally to have been everywhere quite common, yet the literature does not suggest the existence of the marked concentrations such as are often reported elsewhere. There were several favored nesting islands, however, to which turtlers repaired in season. Oviedo mentions especially Cubagua and other nearby islands off the north coast of Venezuela (*162*:lib. xix, cap. ii). Père Labat says that the French went especially to the "Iles de la Tortille" (Aves?) and other sparsely inhabited islands (*125*:1:99-102). The turtlers spent three to four months at these Iles de la Tortille taking greens and hawksbills, so they may have been some distance away. The Caymans also suggest themselves, but elsewhere Labat refers to the Caymans by name. Rochefort, on the other hand, points to St. Martin's as a particular good turtling area (*179*:1:26), while for Dampier "the best in the West Indies, both for largeness and sweetness" were found at Isla Blanco off the north coast of Venezuela where they "come up to lay in great abundance" (*53*: 1:87). Later accounts suggest that Isla Mona (*112*), off Puerto Rico, and Isla Aves, west of Guadeloupe, were also important nesting grounds. There is a Huevos Island at the northwest tip of Trinidad that is said to be named for its turtle eggs, but these may have been of the hawksbill kind, as were those taken on Barbados. Carr reports that on the windward beaches of Trinidad, near Mayaro, there was once a big green-turtle rookery. Today they come up but seldom, perhaps because of the steady catching of nesting females, or perhaps because the roots of coconut trees, bared by the erosive action of waves, are making it increasingly difficult for the females to make their nests (*34*:114-15, 122).

Green turtles formerly laid in considerable numbers, as they still may, on certain sections of the Guiana coast. Lacépède quotes a French resident physician to the effect that about 300 live greens were taken each year between April and June near Cayenne where they came to lay. This was at the end of the eighteenth century (*126*:125-27). Stedman, about the same time, describes green-turtle meat "publicly exposed to sale by the butchers in Surinam like the shambles meat in European markets [and] esteemed as the most delicious between February and May" (*198*:1:16). Green turtles are still not uncommon along the Guiana coast, especially at Biggi Santi (Big Sandy) beach between Paramaribo and the Moroni River in Surinam, and in British Guiana west of the Courantyne mouth.

Their former abundance in Curaçao waters is evidenced by an order in 1737 restricting the slaughter of green turtles to certain streets in Willemstadt because of the offensive odors this activity produced (*114*:14; *17*:202). Today one would have to walk a long way to see a turtle slaughtered on Curaçao or the other Dutch islands. The few that are taken by drift nets or harpoons are believed to be migrants. The latest reference to commercial exploitation of nesting turtles in this area that I have encountered is an account published in 1911 of activities on the desert island of Blanquilla (*138*:177). The island, which lies fifty miles north of Margarita, at that time was leased by the Venezuelan government to an entrepreneur who was curing turtle and goat meats and packing them in large jars for shipment to the mainland.

I have found no specific reference to turtles on Isla Tortuga or the small Islas Tortuguillas off the north coast of Venezuela. The names may have been inspired by their shape, as has been suggested to have been the case with the buccaneer-frequented Isla Tortuga (Ile Tortue) on the northwest coast of Hispaniola. The Hispaniola "La Tortuga," however, is known through a letter written in 1495 by Michele de Cuneo to have been given by Columbus, on the first voyage, to commemorate the taking of a giant turtle there (*17a*:103).

On both coasts of Hispaniola turtles, either hawksbills or greens, were extremely abundant in the first years of the Spanish occupation. *"Tartuge infinitissime, grosissime . . . optime al mangiare"* ("an infinity of giant turtles . . . optimal for eating"), wrote the Italian Cuneo of them in 1495 (*17a*: 101). There are frequent references to them in the journal of Columbus and in the works of Oviedo and Peter Martyr. The last author, the first chronicler of Spain in the Caribbean, described in terms of wonderment (Decade IV, Book 9) the reports he had heard of the mass nesting of sea turtles on the island of Alta Vela off the southwest coast of Hispaniola near Cabo Beata (*144*:1:391). Later accounts make no mention of turtles on Alta Vela, but before the English had arrived and become so closely associated with turtles, the Spaniards seem to have eaten the meat with gusto. Indeed it seems to have been Martyr who first used what was to become the standard descriptive phrase for turtle meat when he termed it the equivalent of veal (*ternero*).

Possibly the most important single surviving green-turtle nesting beach in the eastern Caribbean area today is tiny, uninhabited Isla Aves, 130 miles west of Guadeloupe and 350 miles north of the Venezuelan mainland. Briefly, in the 1850's, it was the subject of litigation among five nations, all of whom coveted it for its guano (*214*; this is a 472-page collection of correspondence concerning the question). Venezuela's claims were in the end recognized, but the islet has never been permanently occupied. A United States Air Force mapping group, on Aves in 1954 to pinpoint it as a geodetic link between North and South America, ran into unexpected trouble—turtles. During the first two weeks of July an average of twenty big greens a night lumbered ashore, knocking down radio masts and so disturbing the camp that the personnel had to be taken off the island each evening. A few turtles were still coming ashore in October and November, when the unit returned after an absence of two and one-half months, but by the end of December all turtle activity had ceased.*

A schooner of about thirty tons gross and a smaller sloop, both operated by a St. Lucian, sail between Aves and Dominica carrying turtles to Dominica during the three summer months. The schooner carries fifty to sixty turtles on each trip and makes up to six trips during a season. Occasionally other boats may carry turtles to Dominica, so that annual receipts there probably exceed 400 animals a year. The turtles are turned on the Aves beach and carried alive to the market, water being thrown on them during the voyage. On arrival they are kept in a fresh-water pond until needed. They weigh mostly between 250 and 300 pounds. In 1959 the official price was eight cents (B.W.I.) per pound alive, but they were being sold on the black market for twelve to fourteen cents per pound and retailed by butchers at twenty-five cents. Some of the animals are sent to St. Lucia where the meat is locally consumed and the calipee and calipash are dried and shipped to London.† Lindeman reported that 200 turtles were being shipped annually in the 1870's from St. Lucia to London (*134*:86).

It is probable that the turtle population of Aves is much reduced from its former levels. Its establishment as a "turtle reserve" has recently been suggested by Venezuelan interests (*181*). But any such remedy may in the end prove futile, for the island seems to be gradually disappearing under the sea. When Père Labat was on Aves in 1705 he described it as a considerable island, two leagues (*lièves*) by three leagues in dimension and with a maximum elevation of some 45 feet. A recent survey shows it to be now scarcely 1,500 feet long, its maximum elevation 10 feet. Labat, who found an abundance of nesting turtles there, found the island supporting a vegetation that included guavas (*goyaviers*), soursops (*corossoliers*), and custard apples (*cachimans*). Today there is nothing but common purslane growing there. The area of sand suitable for nesting turtles is doubtless much reduced as a result of this drastic alteration of the island's shoreline. Should it com-

---

* Personal correspondence, June 26, 1958, from Major William C. Rogers, Hq., 1370th Photo-Mapping Group, Palm Beach Air Force Base; see also *133*.

† Information on the Dominica and St. Lucia trade is from William Clarke, Alameda State College, California.

pletely founder, the Aves turtles will be faced with a dilemma of considerable proportions and one which would be of much interest to students of animal behavior (240).

THE COAST OF BRAZIL

The tropical coasts of Brazil, from the mouth of the Amazon southward to Rio de Janeiro, are intermittently visited by nesting green turtles, but information regarding their numbers and distribution is scarce. Here, as elsewhere on southern hemisphere beaches, the main egg-laying season is from December to March or April. The seaward side of Marajó Island, at the mouth of the Amazon, is apparently an important nesting zone. Others have been described north and south of the Rio Doce (Vitória) and at Cabo Frio, near Rio de Janeiro (81:720). *Chelonia mydas* are also reported to frequent certain localities in Bahia, Parahyba, and other places on the north coast. Of the beaches with which Emilio Goeldi was familiar the most favored was the 50-mile stretch between the Rio Doce and Rio São Matheus and another between the Rio Riacho and the Rio Mucury. He also mentions Prado, Comechatiba, Trancoso, and Pôrto Seguro as places frequented by turtles. Many of these may have been hawksbills.

Prince Maximilian of Wied in 1816-17 described these deserted and inhospitable beaches of tropical Brazil, then visited only by Indians during the egg-laying season (230:95, 103). Piles of bleached turtle skeletons contributed to their melancholy aspect. The Tupi called the green turtle *suruaná*. They were apparently more interested in it for its eggs and oil than for the meat, an attitude also noted toward the freshwater Amazon river turtle. It will be remembered that the Portuguese, like the Spaniards, seem to have had but little interest in turtles, and this is further suggested by the infrequency of reference to them in the Brazilian literature. It seems probable, however, that the mainland beaches, however isolated, did not offer sufficiently favorable protection from man and other predators to permit the build-up of large breeding stocks at any one place.

Clearly not so inhospitable to greens was the isolated island of Trinidade, located in the South Atlantic Ocean some 700 miles off the Brazilian coast (20° 23′ S.). Whether the Trinidade turtles were ever commercially exploited I have been unable to establish, but in view of the island's position astride the sailing route from the Guinea coast it seems probable that they were. A British treasure-hunting expedition on the island in the 1890's at Christmas time reported that "female turtle frequent Southwest Bay in large numbers for the purpose   39 of depositing their eggs" (122:183). A few years later another party reported seeing large numbers of turtles close to the rocks off South Trinidade in the month of January (156:39). None were observed to haul out on the beach to lay, perhaps because of the roughness of the surf. I have found no other references to the Ilha Trinidade turtle population, but there is a Ponta das Tartarugas and a Parcel das Tartarugas on modern maps of the island. The rockiness of its shore seems to have barred nesting turtles from the otherwise attractively located Brazilian island of Fernando de Noronha off Cape São Roque.

ASCENSION ISLAND

In the English mind green turtles have always been peculiarly associated with the lonely and barren volcanic island of Ascension. Lying in the South Atlantic Ocean at 8° South latitude, more than 1,000 miles off the Guinea coast of Africa, it early became a watering and victualing place for ships homeward-bound from East India. Its coasts are mostly cliffed and rocky, but there are a few beaches composed entirely of small, rounded pieces of shell that are assaulted each year from February through April by large numbers of nesting green turtles. In the days of sail they provided a welcome respite from salt provisions and hardtack.

The Ascension turtles attracted special attention for their size as well as their numbers, and there are several reports, apparently not exaggerated, of specimens weighing 800 pounds or more. Such early chroniclers as Dampier and Captain Cook were impressed by the great distance and the pinpoint navigation skills involved in the Ascension turtle migration. Dampier, noting the absence of turtle-grass, thought they could not find feed anywhere along the steeply shelving coast of the island. "After laying time," he wrote, "you never see them" (53:1:391). Several observers have commented on the apparent absence of males, but it is certain that here as elsewhere the males must mill about at some distance offshore during the egg-laying season. The best guess is that these turtles spend the greater part of their lives browsing in the shallow waters of Brazil or Africa. But how they are able to find their way to so distant and isolated an island must stand as one of Nature's more perplexing secrets. In what manner and when this remarkable behavior pattern may have originated are no more answerable questions.

Ascension Island also attained a certain notoriety among nineteenth-century scientists for the fossil turtle eggs found there cemented in coral, as reported by Sir Charles Lyell.

These, however, need not necessarily have been of any great antiquity.

The earliest reference that I have found to the Ascension turtles was made by a Dutch party that took turtles on the island in the year 1600 (*119*:50:217-19; 46:154). When John Fryer was there sometime between 1672 and 1681 his men turned a total of 120 of the creatures on the beach at night with handspikes, "the flesh of some being as much as our little Indian bullocks." Ship crews, he observed, "mightily lament the want of them when they are spent, because they must return again to their salt meats" (*73*:185). It was chiefly the English and French vessels that called at Ascension, the Dutch most often being provisioned at the Cape, but Roggeveen was there in 1773 and noted of the turtles that the sailors never tired of them, "for they make a perfect change of their juices, freeing them entirely from the scurvy and other diseases of the blood" (*87*:1929:7). In the same year Bernardin de St. Pierre, who stopped there en route home from Mauritius, told of fifty turtles being turned on Ascension in a night. They were so large that they had to be taken aboard ship the next day by a high-line to avoid the rough seas. "For near a month thereafter," he wrote, "we lived wholly upon these turtles, which were kept alive ... sometimes on their back and sometimes on their belly, by throwing sea water over them several times a day." He saw several turtles that had been left on their backs to perish by earlier visitors, "a negligence altogether unpardonable of which thoughtless sailors are too often guilty" (*18*:273, 290).

Green turtles must have been early introduced into England and France by homeward-bound sailing ships out of the East Indies. The first account of this sort that I am aware of is in 1753, when the *Gentleman's Magazine* recorded that, "The turtler Captain Crayton, lately arrived [in London] from the Island of Ascension, has brought several turtles weighing above 300 pounds which have been sold at a very high price" (*77*: 23:441). Oliver Goldsmith, noting that turtles were found "in greatest numbers" at Ascension (ca. 1770), states that they were also salted there "to feed the slaves" (*82*:674). Later accounts indicate that there was a gallows between the two "ponds" in which turtles were kept, where they were slaughtered in preparation for salting. When Captain Cook stopped at Ascension in the 1770's he found a New York sloop there taking on turtles for Barbados. The week previous another, out of Bermuda, had departed with a capacity load of 105 greens. The demand for turtle in the American colonies was by then apparently greater than the supply, although Cook suspected that the Americans might be covering up clandestine trading activities with returning East India ships by their turtling activities (48:67).

The island remained uninhabited until after the arrival of Napoleon at St. Helena, when the British government took possession of Ascension and established a small garrison there. Thereafter the turning of turtles on its beaches became a government monopoly. An observer in 1835 relates that their numbers and sizes "staggered one's belief" (3). In one year more than 2,500 turtles were reported turned on Ascension's beaches. At the height of the season 40 or 50 were normally turned each night. Two men were stationed at each of the three or four most frequented beaches for this task, the turtles being carted to the "ponds" at the settlement the next day. Later a small steam vessel was employed in a coast-wise trade collecting turtles, as members of the "Challenger" expedition noted when they were there in 1876. For the few years for which there are records in the 1840's and 1850's exports of live turtles from Ascension ranged from 600 to 800 annually—750 in 1834, 600 in 1850, 650 in 1853 (87:1932). The figure had been reduced to 300 by 1878, perhaps in part because of the reduction in number of ships calling at the island after the opening of the Suez Canal and the introduction of steam navigation. At this time the turtle-turners, who were government employees, received a half crown for each turtle turned. They were required to wait until the eggs had been laid before the females were turned (79:76; 190:225). An average of only 60 turtles a year were exported during the 1920's, and after 1932 there is no mention of exports in the Colonial Office reports. The latest report for St. Helena, of which Ascension is a dependency, simply states that at Ascension "turtles abound at certain seasons and the catching of them is controlled by license."

The apparent lack of reference to the collection of turtle eggs on Ascension is undoubtedly explained by the extraordinary abundance there of sooty terns ("wide-awakes"), whose eggs were sometimes gathered in tremendous quantities, as many as 10,000 dozen being taken in a single week during the breeding season (204:264). The difficulties that the United States Air Force had with these birds during World War II, when an airbase was built on Ascension, is described by James Chapin (44).

There apparently has been some reduction in the numbers of turtles calling at Ascension, though available accounts are inconclusive on this score. For some time now the pressure has been off and it is possible that the Ascension greens may have been successfully rebuilding their population, which late nineteenth-century observers thought to have been substantially reduced from earlier times. A Colonial Office report of 1926 states that "the turtle seemingly no longer land in the vicinity of the town, while at the more remote beaches to the northwest and southeast where they formerly nested in the hundreds they are now only to be found in the tens" (87:21). The amazing Ascension turtles, whose built-in direction finders carry them probably several times in the course of their lifetime across 1,000 miles of open sea to this remote oceanic island, await the attention of biologists and conservationists.

THE CAPE VERDE ISLANDS

Ascension has its counterpart north of the equator in the Cape Verde island group (15° N.), some 250 miles off the African coast, where a similar mass influx of nesting green turtles was recorded by numerous early writers and presumably still occurs. The beaches of the drier, eastern islands of the archipelago, especially Sal, Boavista, and Maio, are those most commonly mentioned in connection with green turtles. The rainy months of May through August are the nesting months, in contrast with Ascension, where the season starts at Christmas time. The feeding grounds of these Cape Verde turtles are presumably along the mainland coast of Africa from Mauritania southward, but whether there is intermingling with the Ascension population on the Guinea coast will only be determined by an extensive tagging program.

It was from the Cape Verde Islands that we find the first reference by Europeans to the edible sea turtle. When the Venetian Cadamosto, in the service of Prince Henry the Navigator, discovered this group, site of the most ancient tropical colony of the modern world, in April or May, 1456, he found large numbers of turtles whose meat his party tested and found good, "not unlike the white flesh of veal." On Santiago Island they accordingly salted many of them "because they made good provisions for the voyage." Some of his sailors, he noted, had eaten similar turtles, "although not of such size," on earlier occasions along the mainland coast to the north, especially in the Gulf of Arguin. These sea turtles, Cadamosto wrote, were "what we call *gajandre*" (30:65). I do not know the origin of this presumably Italian term.

The French explorer Eustache de la Fosse, who visited the African coast in 1479, reported that leprosy was cured in those areas by a diet of turtle flesh and by rubbing the affected parts of the skin with turtle blood. On the basis of this report, Louis XI, King of France, believing he had leprosy, sent his representative to the Cape Verde Islands and the Barbary Coast in 1483 to investigate. But the King died, although not from

43

leprosy, before his emissary's return. In 1506 and again in 1508 we hear of Portuguese lepers (*gafos*) being brought to the islands to regain their health eating turtle meat, since during the summer "great numbers of turtles [*tartarugas*] make their nests on these islands" (*224:84; 70:40*). Peter Simmonds mentions that syphilitics were often sent there from Portugal "to be cured by feeding on turtle flesh" (*190:225*). This of course contradicts the general impression of Portuguese disinterest in turtles suggested earlier. On this apparently more evidence is necessary. There are several Dutch references to turtles on the Cape Verdes toward the end of the sixteenth century and the early years of the seventeenth century, but there is no indication that they were any more than casually exploited.

Dampier was on Maio, in the eastern Cape Verdes, in 1683 and again in 1699, loading salt, and he noted that the blacks who lived on the island's beaches made a business of turning turtles during the rainy season and working during the remainder of the year (*53:1:103-5; 2:365-67*). Most of the salt was destined for Newfoundland. He considered the turtles here smaller and less sweet than those of the West Indies, but other observers thought the reverse to be true. François Leguat turned turtles on the Cape Verde beaches in November, 1690, and observed that some of these "stupid and slow creatures . . . according to the guess of the most skillful weighed 500 pounds each" (*130:82:13*). During the height of the season, he wrote, "all the shoar is covered with these animals," which seemed to have been much preferred for provisions to the goats which inhabited the islands in such prodigious quantities. It is noteworthy that Francis Drake, who was at the Cape Verdes in January and again in May, 1577, made no mention of turtles. He was impressed instead with the goats that overran the islands (*64*).

There appears to have been a seasonal migration of the residents of the more populous western Cape Verdes, especially from São Nicoláo, Santiago, and Santo Antão, to Sal Island to take turtle, either for their own use or to sell as salted provision to passing ships. In August, 1724, a French vessel was reported by Captain Roberts at Sal catching the turtles "which come to this island in great numbers," having brought thirty hands from a neighboring island to assist in catching and curing them. There were turtles on Maio, Captain Roberts observed, "but not in any great quantity." At San Juan (?), St. Phillips (Fogo), and St. Jago (Santiago) turtles also came ashore to lay, but were not much regarded as provender, "and yet at all the other islands they are accounted their most delicious food; and indeed, so they are" (*177:390-92,*

402). Portuguese ships also carried salted turtle to Brazil, large quantities having been salted down and sent to feed slaves there in the seventeenth century (45:788).

I have found no first-hand references to turtles on the Cape Verde Islands in recent literature. However, M. Alexandrino, the director of the Sal airport, informs me (March 8, 1959) that they still come ashore to nest on Sal's beaches during the months of August and September, "although not in great numbers." Some of these, at least, are loggerheads rather than greens. Indeed, J. Cadenat, marine biologist at the Institut Français d'Afrique Noire in Dakar, informs me (May 11, 1959) that on his several trips to the Cape Verdes he has never observed *Chelonia mydas*, although an occasional loggerhead (*Caretta caretta*) has been seen. There is no commercial exploitation of the turtles, but local people are said to appreciate both the eggs and the meat. It seems probable that we are dealing here with another green-turtle population that has been sharply reduced in numbers as a result of man's activities. The Cape Verde turtles, like those of Ascension, are crying for a historical and ecological study.

There are frequent references in the literature to the taking of green turtles along the shoal waters of the African coast by both Europeans and Africans, but these feeding grounds seem to have been subject to little commercial exploitation. A small turtle industry is said to have existed in recent years at Requins in Senegal. Both eggs and meat are eaten by the native populations, who use both harpoon and net to take the browsing reptiles. Occasional strays may be turned on their backs as they come ashore to lay, especially between June and August near Dakar and from October to January on the Guinea coast. The Gulf of Arguin (20° N.) and the coast of Ghana, where a rocky bottom promotes a better growth of turtle-grass and seaweed than elsewhere, are two sections of the mainland African coast that are especially frequented by turtles. There is a small Turtle Island off the coast of Sierra Leone that was formerly said to have been much favored for egg taking.* Villiers describes the utilization of turtles along the West African coast (224:71-79).

SEYCHELLES, THE KENYA-SOMALI COAST, AND MOZAMBIQUE CHANNEL

When the first Europeans arrived there, the warm waters of the Indian Ocean abounded in both hawksbill and green turtles. The fine tortoise shell of the Somali coast, the Maldives,

* Personal communication, J. Tomlinson, West African Fisheries Research Institute, Freetown, Sierra Leone, January 7, 1956.

45

and Ceylon had been known in the Mediterranean as a trade item at least since the early Roman Empire. It had provided the lining for Cleopatra's bath and the combs for the emperors' ladies. When Alexandria was taken by Julius Caesar, the warehouses were found so full of tortoise shell that he proposed to have it made the principal ornament of his triumph (25:5:217). In later times it was an important item in the Chinese trade (228:81-83; 28:1:935).

But with the coming of European ships the abundant and delectable green turtle attracted the primary attention. The uninhabited Mascarene Islands—Réunion, Mauritius, and Rodriguez—early became way stations for the provisioning of vessels on the route to India and the East. From numerous early reports it is apparent that green turtles were abundant about each of these islands and that they hauled up on the beaches in large numbers to lay. (See especially the many references in Grandidier and Grandidier, 83.) While it is not always clear whether early writers were referring to the green turtle, the hawksbill (*Eretmochelys imbricata*), or to giant Mascarene land tortoises, there can be no doubt that the *tortues* described as so abundant were most frequently meant to mean *Chelonia mydas*. In 1691 Leguat could still speak of the "prodigious numbers" of sea turtles at Rodriguez, while those at Réunion would have been sufficient "to abundantly and deliciously subsist the inhabitants." He wrote that some of the marine turtles both at Rodriguez and at Réunion weighed above 500 pounds. The land tortoises were smaller but no less numerous. On Rodriguez he described a herd of from 2,000 to 3,000 of the latter, stating with perhaps some exaggeration that "one might go 100 paces on their backs without setting a foot on the ground!" Their flesh he thought very delicate, the fat better than butter or the best oil, being "an excellent remedy for several distempers" (*130*:83:71-72).

At Mauritius, however, sea turtles were by then less common, although only fifty years earlier Van Dieman had proposed the sale of turtle meat to Surat and Coromandel as a promising source of profit to the Dutch who then occupied Mauritius (83:2:498). By the end of the eighteenth century, if not before, the green turtle had become rare in Mascarene waters, threatening to go the way of the extinct dodo, the solitaire bird, the dugong, and the giant land tortoises which, like it, had served to provision sailing ships bound to or from the East. The meat for the turtle broth that the French hospital on Ile de France (Mauritius) fed its scurvy patients was by this time coming from the less extensively exploited Seychelles waters to the north. Today Mauritius obtains what turtles it consumes, some 300 to 600 individuals a year, from isolated St. Brandon's Island, its dependency 300 miles to the north.

The greatest concentration of breeding turtles in the Indian Ocean in modern times, and perhaps in antiquity, has been at the raised atoll of Aldabra and the adjacent smaller islands of Assumption and Cosmoledo, which together comprise the Aldabra group, politically appendages of the British colony of Seychelles since 1810. Assumption, a guano-covered sand bar, lies 20 miles to the south of Aldabra, while Cosmoledo, a tiny atoll, is 60 miles to its east. The Aldabra group lies 200 nautical miles northwest of Madagascar, 620 miles from East Africa, and 760 miles southeast of Mahé, principal island of the Seychelles Archipelago. While turtles are by no means rare among the more northerly and more populous high islands of the Seychelles, it is the arid southern islands that originally were teeming nesting grounds for *Chelonia mydas* from December through March or April of each year. This part of the Indian Ocean, somewhat north of the early routes of trade, seems to have been but little exploited for its green turtles until quite recent times, unless by unrecorded Arab visitors. According to Sir Robert Scott, the governor of Ile de France sent several expeditions to Agalega (southeast of Aldabra) to look for turtles between 1779 and 1787; and for some years before that, country ships from the island had been visiting the Seychelles in search of tortoise shell, turtles, and coconuts (*185*:97, 76). But the earliest reference that I have found to the serious exploitation of those on Aldabra dates from 1847, when a party of a hundred men on two ships is reported to have taken 1,200 greens "in a short time," some weighing 800 pounds (*169*). In 1862 the United States consul at Mauritius stated that 1,800 green turtles had been killed in the Seychelles to obtain 600 pounds of *cawan,* the yellow plates from the plastron, and that nearly 500,000 pounds of flesh had been left to rot on the beach. This, too, appears to have been on Aldabra. He predicted that sooner or later the turtles would abandon the islands "to seek a more undisturbed retreat in which to lay their eggs" (*109*:35-36).

Briefly in the 1870's, a group of Norwegians apparently occupied the theretofore uninhabited 18-mile-long atoll. A group of twenty-seven adults and thirteen children sailed from Bergen in July, 1879, to establish a colony on Aldabra. They were to be joined by another party of their countrymen at Nosy Bé, off Madagascar. The fate of these Norwegians is unknown (*169*).

Regular commercial exploitation of the Aldabra sea turtles, however, did not begin until 1906. (This section is greatly indebted to James Hornell, *109*; see also *156*:103.) That year the island was leased to one Walter Rothschild who imported African laborers to plant coconuts and catch turtles. From this time begins the export of dried calipee. The average 300-pound turtle yields about 3½ pounds of sun-dried calipee, in addition to perhaps 60 pounds of salted turtle meat (*quitouze*) for the local Seychelles market. The calipee traditionally has gone to the London soup makers, but the *quitouze* and any turtles kept live have been marketed in Mahé and the other northern Seychelles islands. From time to time small quantities of turtle oil have been exported as well as shell, bones, and blood for fertilizer and a *tortue marinade*, fried turtle meat packed in oil and shipped in casks.

A commission of inquiry in 1909 said that some 1,500 live turtles arrived yearly at Mahé for butchering and that these probably represented no more than one third of the number originally put aboard the schooners that carried them, so great was the mortality rate on the five-day trip. Some live turtles were already being brought from as far away as the volcanic Europa Island (22° 20′ S., 40° 20′ E.) in Mozambique Channel, nearly 1,500 miles distant from Mahé. In the latter place the meat was said to be "a staple and highly valued article of diet, taking there the place that beef occupies in Europe."

The all-time high for calipee exports from Seychelles appears to have been reached in 1912 when official statistics show that 36,900 pounds were shipped, equivalent to at least 9,000 turtles. Normally all calipee is exported (i.e., not wasted or consumed when the flesh is consumed locally), so that calipee exports provide a reasonable basis for estimating the total turtle catch.* In this period it was said to be common to turn 50 greens in a night at Aldabra, and almost as many at Assumption, where on one record night 400 are reported to have been taken. Although Cosmoledo probably never attained the annual yield of 7,000 turtles recently credited to it by William Travis in his account of green-snail collecting in the western Indian Ocean, it was certainly a significant producer (*211*:149; this figure apparently derives from *164*:296, and must be presumed a misprint). There has been a progressive decline in the numbers of turtles captured in the southern Seychelles during the past forty years. During the 1920's and 1930's the number seems to have ranged from 3,000 to 4,000 annually, mostly from Aldabra, while the figure since World War II has been closer to 1,500. Calipee exports averaged

* Personal communication, A. Jefferies, Department of Agriculture, Mahé, Seychelles, April 13, 1956.

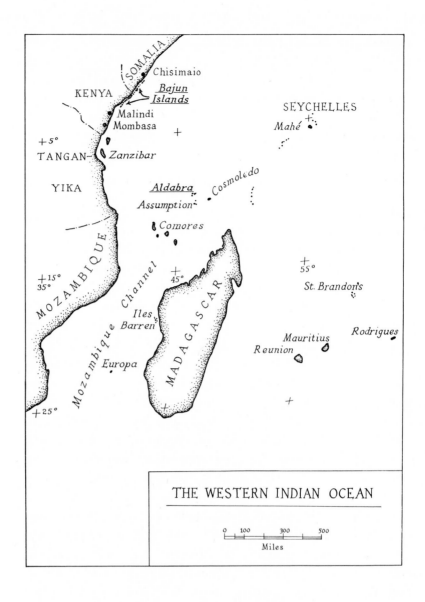

THE WESTERN INDIAN OCEAN

0   100   300   500
Miles

about 4,500 to 5,000 kilograms during the 1930's, according to government reports. In 1956 the figure was 3,000 kilograms, but London trade sources consider this figure too low. By the latter date the export of turtle oil and salted turtle meat appears to have ceased, as had the export of tortoise shell.

On Cosmoledo green turtles are said to be comparatively rare, while they have practically vanished from Assumption where Travis reports that fewer than 30 a month of the big greens are seen off its shore during the season (211:205). The much larger Aldabra is leased to a private company that keeps a seventy-man crew there during the season, drying turtle meat and calipee on great drying trays. No live turtles are exported from the Seychelles, but in addition to calipee small quantities of that universally prized elixir, turtle oil, occasionally are listed in the trade statistics.

49

Official concern for the eventual fate of the Seychelles green-turtle population dates at least from 1925, when a turtle ordinance was passed prohibiting egg collection and the taking of undersized turtles. James Hornell, who was commissioned at this time to make a study of the industry, wrote that the Aldabra lessees were "pushing to the utmost," taking every turtle possible to compensate for the low price and small demand for guano, which was their primary concern at the time. The lessees' policy of indiscriminate and unrestrained slaughter, he wrote, could not but lead to the early extinction of the trade. He recommended stringent protective measures, including a closed season, continued protection of eggs, and protection from such natural enemies of the young as the frigate bird. He also urged that in the future the lessees be required to deliver a certain number of live turtles to Mahé to ensure a supply of fresh meat to that market, which often found itself without it.

Conditions, however, seem not to have materially improved. A commission, which supported the earlier proposals of Hornell, concluded in 1948 that "the fishery of the green turtle is following the familiar pattern of commercial exploitation, a pattern carried to its melancholy conclusion with the northern right whale and almost as far with the southern hump back, the fur seals of the Pribilofs, the Falklands and Patagonia, the elephant seals of South Georgia and even, one may add, the marketable bottom fish of the North Sea" (229).

Today there is a closed season at Aldabra from December through February, the principal laying months. No turtles may be harpooned at any time under the light of a torch or within 1,000 meters of the high-tide mark, and no eggs may be taken or sold at any time of the year. Assumption, together with one part of Aldabra, has been set aside as an undisturbed breeding ground and sanctuary. No government officials are stationed on the islands, however, so that control is far from complete (A. Jefferies). Mr. Harry Savy, a well-known Seychellois, obtained a fifty-year lease on the Aldabra group in 1954. "Turtles are now scarce compared with earlier in the century," a recent Colonial Office report for Seychelles cryptically notes, "doubtless due to overexploitation." It seems possible, however, that a sustained yield program may yet be instituted here if conservation-minded officials continue to find support for their programs.

Depradations by sharks seem to be especially serious at Aldabra. Travis commented on the large numbers of turtles he saw here that were missing a flipper, usually one of the hind ones. He believes that these almost certainly have been bitten off by sharks, which are said to prefer turtle meat to all other. A hook baited to turtle flesh, he observes, will invariably attract a shark when all other lures have failed. The very large schools of sharks here, he believes, explain his observation that the turtles carry on love-making only when the moon is bright, and then only in comparatively shallow waters. But even these precautions do not always provide them full security (211:168-69).

There are no extensive shoal waters around Aldabra to provide grazing for the vegetarian green turtle, and it has been surmised by Hornell and others that the great hordes resorting to the Aldabras to breed come from pastures in the Mozambique Channel. Hornell has pointed to the abundant fat that the animals carry as a food reserve which may especially fit them for long-distance migrations (109:41-44). This thesis is also accepted by F. D. Ommanney (161). Ship captains are said to report large numbers of green turtles in the channel from May to August. The species is known to occur at least as far south as Durban, where the creatures occasionally become enmeshed in shark nets placed along the beaches for the safety of bathers, but there appears to be no commercial interest in them.* Green turtles do still nest on the Mozambique and Kenya coasts, but there are no accounts of the numbers involved or the locality of this activity. They may be only random strays from the main breeding population that resorts to the Aldabra group.

Formerly sea turtles nested in substantial numbers along the more protected north and west coasts of Madagascar, at Europa Island, on the Comores, and on the Kenya and Somali offshore islands, but nesting today is said to be relatively rare, apparently because of the long continued activities of turtle turners and egg collectors. In 1923 six islets off the west coast of Madagascar (Nosy Anambo, Nosy Iranja, Chesterfield, Nosy Trozana, Nosy Bé, and Europa) were set aside by French authorities as turtle reserves. Elsewhere the taking of nesting turtles before they had laid, and of any turtle less than 50 centimeters (20 inches) long, was forbidden. But the measures are said to have been ineffective because of the impossibility of surveillance (55:201). Not mentioned, perhaps because they had already been stripped clean of turtles, were the uninhabited Barren Islands (Iles Stériles, 18° 30′ S., 43° 50′ E.) where Padre Luis Mariano in 1613 reported "great numbers of turtles," apparently laying congregations.

The Malagasy are said to be equally fond of turtle eggs and turtle meat, especially that of the greens. Most of the latter

* Personal correspondence, P. A. Clancy, Director, Durban Museum and Art Gallery, December 15, 1955.

are now taken by harpoon from outrigger canoes. Among the Sakalava, hardy sailors who have hunted turtles since time immemorial, the turtle chase is the principal sport. They maintain special altars on the beach that are consecrated to the turtle, which is considered to be sacred. Among the Vezo of the southwest coast early morning ceremonial rites, preliminary to the turtle hunt, are held in specially built beach huts (*rantsanas*). Stray nesting females are still turned on the beaches where the opportunity arises, much as they were by Arab navigators who came to Madagascar for this purpose as long ago as the ninth and tenth centuries. A good turtle turner (*mpianbinjia*) may turn 10 to 15 turtles in an average season, but this would probably include hawks-bills as well as greens (*218*:74-86; *84*; *55*:95-98; G. Petit in *88*:1948).

The principal center of turtling activities on the African coast is the Bajun Islands of Kenya and Somaliland, whose inhab-itants take green turtles with the aid of suckerfish, or remora (*Echeneis*), which, tied to a long leash, are let out to at-tach themselves to the carapace of the feeding greens (*94*: 324-29; see also Chapter 3). Until recently this type of turtling was carried on by the Bajuni only to meet their own need for meat, but since 1950 exports of live turtles to England, especially, have taken on major proportions. From 1954 to 1959 between 1,000 and 1,500 live turtles have been exported annually from Kenya, perhaps half of the total Bajuni catch. A substantial but unknown share of these are taken off the Somali coast immediately to the north and brought to Kenya for re-export. Bajuni fishermen are said to be supplying most of the live turtles and frozen carcasses entering English mar-kets, almost all being taken in this singular fashion.

Due to the initiative of the Kenya Coast Oyster Company a market also has been found in Britain for turtle oil and "green fat" (calipee) from Kenya. Operations commenced in 1951, and in the following year a small turtle-soup cannery was opened. By 1954 it was estimated that 200 turtles were being slaughtered annually on the Kenya coast to supply this new plant (*116*:1951:46; 1952:75; 1953:30; 1954:31).

Concern for the future of the turtle industry led, in 1959, to green turtles being declared "Royal game" in Kenya, and their capture is now controlled by a special system of permits. The turning of turtles on the beach is strictly prohibited, and immature turtles with a carapace of less than twenty-four inches are completely protected. Under current regulations licenses to capture turtles are being granted only to skippers of boats who have traditionally engaged in this fishery, using suckerfish. In 1958 a total of twenty-three skippers held licenses, of whom fourteen were based at Kizingitini and three each at Malindi and Lamu. There were eleven licensed turtle dealers. The regulations call for the keeping of records showing the size and sex of all turtles taken, together with the place of their capture. It is anticipated that future conservation measures may be based on such information.[*]

THE CENTRAL AND EASTERN INDIAN OCEAN AND DIAMOND ISLAND

Several other islands and island groups north and east of the Seychelles in the Indian Ocean support breeding populations of sea turtles. Masira Island, off the south coast of Arabia, is one of these—"in the spring, at night, very large numbers of turtles come ashore to lay their eggs" (56). It is possible that these are hawksbills, for the Periplus of the Erythraean Sea, written in the first century, refers to the excellent tortoise shell produced on Masira, then called Sarapis. On Masira Island, as on the Laccadives and the Maldives (75: 2:1050), the literature does not always differentiate between green turtles and hawksbills. The latter also is occasionally, if not so characteristically as the green, a social nester.

James Hornell, in 1908, suggested opening up an export trade in fresh turtle from the Laccadives (quoted in 7). Favorite nesting haunts in the Laccadives were earlier reported by W. Robinson to be the uninhabited islands of Bingaram and Tingaram, each of which had a large deep-water lagoon. A third island, Suhely, was a private preserve. He observed that the eggs seemed not to be much eaten (178:65).

François Pyrard, in the Maldives in the seventeenth century, was apparently referring to green turtles when he wrote, "there are vast numbers of them at the Maldives and some little islands you may see inhabited by no other animals than these great turtles, but covered with them. On our arrival at the Maldives we caught a great one with 500 or 600 large eggs, like yellow hen's eggs ... we lived on them for 3-4 days ... the flesh [being] like veal" (171:80:348-49). There was another, smaller kind (hawksbill?) that he described as being "sought after by all the kings and rich people in the Indies, chiefly those of Cambay and Surat." In both the Maldives and the Laccadives, as in Malaya and Borneo, the eating of turtle flesh is taboo, but large numbers of the creatures are harpooned at sea, to be rendered into oil for caulking ships.

[*] Personal correspondence, D. F. Smith, Chief Fisheries Officer, Game Department, Nairobi, March 8, 1959; also 116:1957:9.

53

Chelonia mydas is curiously rare in the Bay of Bengal and on the coasts of India. It does breed occasionally, however, on the eastern Pakistan and Ceylon coasts, along with the more numerous hawksbill and loggerhead. There does not appear to be any well defined nesting concentration. There is a sizeable green-turtle fishery at Jaffna, Ceylon, where twenty to thirty of the animals are slaughtered each Sunday. Although it apparently breeds throughout the year in Ceylon, it is most abundant from January to March and is thus in cycle with the Seychelles population.*

The largest single nesting concentration on the eastern side of the Indian Ocean is apparently at Diamond Island, a low, forested bar at the mouth of the Bassein River, in Burma. An important lighthouse has long been located here. The Burmese, like the Malays, exploit the turtles for their eggs rather than their meat. *The Burma Gazetteer* (1916) says that the eggs are consumed throughout the Irrawaddy delta and by the "well-to-do" in the interior (29). Captain Maxwell's "Report on the Turtle Banks of the Irrawaddy Division" (1898) states that 1.6 million green-turtle eggs, together with 1.5 million additional eggs of the loggerhead, were then being taken yearly from Diamond Island alone by egg collectors working under license from the government (quoted in *194*:65). Such a figure would suggest a population of some 4,000 nesting greens alone being present at any one laying season. Whether or not the current egg harvest is at all comparable to those of the past I do not know. Apparently the ban on taking live turtles has periodically been violated, as during the Burmese Wars when a British ship is said to have been sent to Diamond Island expressly for a cargo of live turtle when scurvy broke out among the troops (*190*:230). Simmonds suggests that the egg harvest was by that time considerably reduced from that of earlier years. "Ten years ago boat loads of turtle eggs were taken to Moulmein. Now a man thinks himself lucky to get a few small basketfuls there." Theobald noted that elsewhere on this coast the loggerhead was the most common turtle. "Few Europeans in Burma," he wrote, perhaps with tongue in cheek, "have any suspicion that the loggerhead is not the real turtle (*i.e.*, Chelonia), or could discriminate the one from the other" (*203*:9). He said that the Calcutta market was largely supplied from the Straits, but that more frequently the loggerhead or the land tortoise of the Irrawaddy delta (*Batagar baska*) was substituted for it at the Chouringhee or Guildhall banquets.

* Personal correspondence, P. E. P. Deraniyagala, Colombo, May 4, 1956; see also 59.

54

Where these Diamond Island greens come from or where they go after the nesting season is not known with certainty. It is said to be the local belief that their home pastures are in the Andaman Islands, not far to the south, where green turtles are described as "especially common." Captain Maxwell was of the opinion that only a small part of the Andaman population visited the Burmese coast in any one year.

Among the Andaman Islanders the green turtle plays an especially important role. Radcliffe-Brown, who describes the turtle eating and turtle-egg eating on North Andaman associated with coming-of-age ceremonies, states that turtle and pork are the two most important foods of the coastal peoples (173:96-102). The creatures are harpooned at sea while feeding and the turtle hunt is an important community undertaking. Although stray females not uncommonly come ashore to lay, they are reported never to be turned on the beach, as such conduct would be "unsportsmanlike" (142:144-45).

Both Cocos-Keeling and Christmas islands, isolated coral patches several hundred miles off the southwest coast of Java, have small breeding populations of greens, apparently now much reduced in size. Captain Cook's party turned forty turtles in a single night at Christmas (10° 30' S.) in 1777, but today they are reported scarce there. On Cocos-Keeling (12° S.), where they were formerly plentiful in the main lagoon, the Malays now manage to harpoon fifteen or twenty in a year and these are of a much smaller size than formerly (78:206).

The green turtle is said still to breed in "considerable numbers" at North Keeling. Some of the Malays, apparently not subject to the taboo against the flesh, are said to place the newly hatched turtles in a tidal pond and feed them until they are large enough to eat.

THE GULF OF SIAM, MALAYA, AND INDONESIA

Although the warm and shallow seas of Southeast Asia appear to offer extraordinarily favorable environmental conditions for *Chelonia mydas*, the long history of the exploitation of the species in this area might have been expected to have disrupted its breeding habits and depleted its numbers. However, despite heavy egg drain, and in contrast to most other areas where they congregate, there is no very clear evidence of permanent depletion of the green-turtle stock. Hendrickson has surmised that the Southeast Asian taboo on turtle slaughter has been responsible for the relatively favorable ecologic situation of the species here as compared to its

55

decreasing population in many other parts of the tropical world (*106:460*).

For the Chinese, however, turtles seem always to have been valued for the fat obtained both from the flesh and from the eggs, and the increasing numbers of Chinese in Southeast Asia may eventually bring damaging pressures on the species. Dampier observed a thriving business in green turtles being conducted at Poulo Condore, an island group off the mouth of the Mekong, by fishermen from Cochin China who took them in nets and rendered them to oil. The chief trade at Poulo Condore he found to be in dammar resin, gathered by Chinese from the mainland. "Some others of them employ themselves to catch turtle and boil up their fat to oil, which they also transport home [to Cochin China]. These people have great nets, with wide meshes, to catch the turtle. The Jamaica turtlers have such, and I did never see the like nets but at Jamaica and here" (*53:1:393, 561-63*). The English had a factory on Poulo Condore in the seventeenth century and may well have exploited the turtles that browsed offshore. There is a reference in 1793 to a solitary green observed nesting on the beach here (*197:1:319*). The turtle industry in this area is today reported to be centered in the Cambodian coastal villages of Samit and Luc-son, near Há-tien, from which several boats equipped with large nets take turtles, both green and hawksbill, during the winter monsoon from November to February. Egg destruction had been so intensive that the government of Cochin China had outlawed the collection, consumption, and sale of turtle eggs in 1923. Before World War II a dozen different Annamite villagers in nearby Há-tien were hatching hawksbill eggs and selling month-old turtles to local "turtle raisers" (*131*). But the weakened market for tortoise shell has probably eliminated this activity in more recent years.

Along the coast of Thailand turtles may be taken to some extent for their meat and oil, but here the principal concern is for the eggs, which bring about double what hen's eggs do. For at least 150 years the privilege of gathering and selling the eggs has been granted by the Thai government to private persons on payment of an annual rental. The offshore islands that serve as nesting beaches are numerous. The most important seem to be Ko Kra (8° 20' N.), eighty miles northeast of Songkhla near the Malayan border, and Ko Kram (12° 40' N.), seventy miles south of the mouth of the Menam on the east side of the Gulf of Thailand (*168*). Turtles nest at Phuket on Thailand's Indian Ocean coast. Pre-World War II sources suggest that removal of turtle eggs had led to a serious reduction in breeding stock, although the blame was placed on the predatory swamp lizard as much as on man. John Crawfurd had noted that the eggs from certain offshore islands constituted "a considerable article of royal revenue" when he was in Siam in 1821 (52:2:196). Virginia Thompson (207:327-28) quotes government records to the effect that the number of breeding turtles had been reduced 80 per cent between 1923 and 1931! But this seems quite unreasonable in the light of experience elsewhere in Southeast Asia. According to Michele Sullivan, Bangkok merchant (personal correspondence, July 15, 1960), eggs are collected under government supervision, being taxed one and a quarter United States cents per kilogram. Although some eggs are taken in every month, the harvest reaches its peak in June, at the height of the rainy season. Both green turtles and hawksbills nest on the same beaches here; the ratio between the two species was 4 to 1 on Ko Kram and about 5 to 3 on Ko Kra in 1956, a bad year when 105,000 eggs were taken on the two islands by licensed collectors (168).

On the east coast of Malaya green turtles habitually nest on several of the more remote offshore islands, and the taking of turtle eggs is a well organized business under the jurisdiction of the local governments, for which it is a source of revenue. In Trengganu the islands of Perhentian, Tenggol, and the Redangs are especially frequented by nesting females, as is Tioman in Pahang (106). Each lies between fifteen and twenty miles off the Malayan coast. Although there seem to be no statistics on the numbers of turtle eggs recovered from Malayan beaches, they apparently run into the millions. Large quantities of the eggs find their way to Singapore markets. On the Malayan islands rats and ghost crabs are the principal predators. While the green turtles stick to the islands, the mainland beaches are frequented by less prized species, especially the leatherback and the ridley (106:461).

There are at least thirty licensed areas for egg collecting on the east coast of Malaya. One area in central Trengganu is used almost exclusively by the leatherback turtle (Dermochelys coriacea), while the beach to the north and south of this, and the offshore islands, are used predominantly by Chelonia mydas. The latter seems to prefer beaches of fine-grained sand, while the leatherback nests where the sands are coarse. In an unpublished paper presented at the Xth Pacific Science Congress, Honolulu, 1961, J. R. Hendrickson and E. Balasingam suggest that this difference in the "feel" of the sand may influence a female turtle's selection of a nesting beach. The coarse beaches are also much steeper than those of fine sand and the linear distance from the sea to nesting sites on the high beach platform is much shorter. The shorter crawl overland may be important to the larger and heavier *Dermochelys*, whose numbers are reported to be much diminished from earlier days.

Although the Malays do not eat turtle flesh, the Chinese living in Singapore and Malaya have no such aversion to it. The turtles that are offered in the Singapore market are apparently taken in fishing stakes and nets off the coast, it being prohibited to turn them on the beaches. The former Federated Malay States Fisheries Ordinance forbade the capture, injury, or possesion of turtles except with authorization and provided for State Rulers' private preserves and for exclusive rights of collection of eggs on specified beaches. In some of the unfederated states there were legal provisions for sanctuaries (*106*:459). In 1961 the eggs were selling at about one pound sterling a hundred.

Green turtles are said to be relatively uncommon in the Strait of Malacca and northward in the Mergui Archipelago, but this may not have always been so. The Malayan islands of Sembilan (*20*:28) and Tulare, as well as the Indonesian-held Aroa group off the Sumatra coast northwest of Singapore, have always been noted as nesting centers (*8*). The last named was reported leased out to egg collectors from Siak as recently as twenty years ago. Egg collectors paid a rent of 1,100 Netherlands guilders for rights on these islands in 1937 when some 215,000 eggs were reported taken. Although the Malayan and Thai islands at the north end of the Strait of Malacca are reported to have nesting beaches, few turtle eggs appear to be marketed from these islands as compared with the larger numbers from the east coast. The populations resorting there may belong to the Indian Ocean breeding community. J. Thompson told of his talk in 1875 with two resident Malayan egg collectors at Poulo Tulare, sixty miles north of Penang. They told him that there was "no stopping" the turtles once they had commenced to lay (*206*:23).

The extensive Dutch literature on Indonesia contains remarkably few references to green turtles. In these waters the hawksbill seems always to have been the more important species, both economically and numerically. The principal modern references that I have found to localized nesting beaches in Indonesian waters relate to the south coast of Java where relatively small-scale egg-collecting activities have persisted at least until recently at Schildpadden Baai in Bantam and on the south coast of Noesa Barung (*219*; *123*; *Soerabaiasch Handelblad*, July 16, 1931). There are in reality two Schildpadden Baais in Bantam, one at 109° 15′ E., the other near Wijnkoops Baai at 106° 30′ E. Kooper thought in 1936 that the turtles there might be threatened with extinction because of the intensive egg-collecting activities of the Javanese and Chinese. Collecting rights on individual beaches were leased out by government authorities. Chinese, Balinese, and Japanese turtle hunters, who, unlike the Javanese, have been after meat as well as eggs, are blamed for the decimation of the formerly profitable egg business on Barung Island.

On the north coast of Java turtles are uncommon today, though a seventeenth-century account by the Dutchman Christopher Fryke describes a large congregation of nesting sea turtles that may have been greens on the small island of Onrust only a few miles from Batavia. Of Onrust, a place for careening ships, he wrote, "the only pastime we could have was catching Tortoises, of which there are vast numbers there. When it is fair, and the sun shines bright, they come out of the water to lie in the hot sand." His party turned them on their backs, pickled them with salt and vinegar, and put them in barrels. "This was our daily food, and very good, but some of 'em are far bigger than others. The biggest we caught was more than three men could compass . . ." (74:89).

On Bali, where Hindu rather than Muslim customs prevail, turtle meat is a festive, though expensive dish (51:105-8).

Dampier, off the southern coast of Celebes (Boeton Island, 5° 30′ S.) in 1687, found an abundance of turtles, though he did not specifically identify them as greens: "We hoisted out our canoa and sent the Moskito men [brought from Central America], of whom we had two or three, to strike turtle, for here there are plenty of them"; and again, off the east coast of Celebes (1° 50′ S.), where he found them especially wily: "Here we stayed several days and sent out our canoas striking for turtle every day; for here is a great plenty of them; but they were very shy, as they were wherever we found them in the East India Seas. I know not the reason for it, unless the natives go very much a-striking here, for even in the West Indies they are shy [only] in places that are much disturbed. And yet on New Holland we found them shy . . . though the natives do not molest them there" (53:1:443, 439). These were quite probably browsing greens, and they may well still be abundant in these shoal waters. Indonesian and Dutch interest, however, traditionally has been focused on the hawksbill. Makassar was long the tortoise-shell emporium of the Indies and Ternate was not far behind it in importance. There are some Schildpad (Turtle) Islands in the Banda Sea (127° 53′ E., 5° 12′ S.) and a large group with the same name in the Gulf of Tomini off the east coast of Celebes, but I have been unable to ascertain whether these names may have related originally to hawksbills or to greens. On the almost uninhabited northwest coast of Borneo (Kalimantan) near the Sarawak border some turtle-egg collecting is carried on under license from the Indonesian government. Predators undoubtedly have played a major role in determining the tenability of Indonesian beaches for turtles. H. C. Raven reports observing the monitor lizard (*Varanus*) raiding *Chelonia* nests on Bilang Bilang Island off the west coast of Borneo (*176*). Wherever the greens lay on the mainland, their eggs are said to be taken by wild pigs (*Sus barbatus*).

THE SARAWAK TURTLE ISLANDS

Probably no green-turtle nesting beaches are so intensively utilized and exploited as those of the Turtle Islands of Sarawak. Certainly the natural history of *Chelonia mydas* has nowhere been placed under more careful scrutiny, thanks to the efforts of the curator of the Sarawak Museum, Tom Harrisson, and of University of Malaya zoologist John Hendrickson (*101; 106*). The two principal islands, Talang Talang Besar and Talang Talang Kechil, lie close together five or six miles off the coast of western Sarawak at the mouth of the Simitar River. The much less frequented Setang Besar is twenty-five miles to the northeast, only a short distance from the capital city of Kuching. Each of these three coconut-covered islands has a small white sand beach on its lee side, and each has a fringing coral reef below mean low-tide level. The restricted extent of these beaches, which in all total no more than six acres, is remarkable in view of the vast numbers of females that haul up on them to lay throughout the year, but especially in the months of March through August. "Over an acre or less," writes Tom Harrisson, "one hundred or more full scale female turtles may stagger, crawl, trample and dig during one night," so that existing nests are not infrequently disturbed or destroyed. It has been shown that the creatures return to the same beach with almost unerring accuracy, so that there are really three distinct populations involved, one for each island. In recent tagging experiments only 3.7 per cent of 5,748 females returning to lay after an average absence of ten days at sea showed a change of island from the previously recorded nesting place. Yet the great majority of the records were concentrated on the two Talang Talang islands, little more than 500 yards apart. Many of the 3.7 per cent are believed to have changed beaches in an attempt to escape the disturbance of being tagged or being examined for tags (*106:497*).

The history of egg collecting on the islands can be traced at least to 1839 with the following diary entry by James

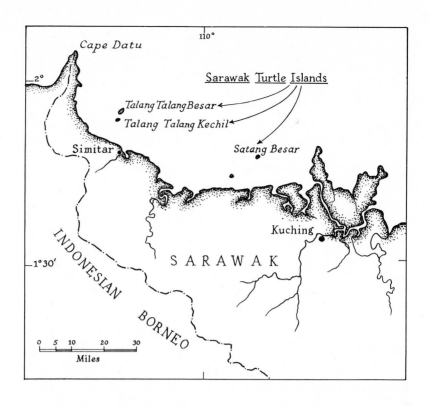

Brooke, later Rajah Brooke I of Sarawak: "Morning calm. In the afternoon got under way and anchored again near the islands of Talang Talang.... The Bandar of the place came off in his canoe to make us welcome. He is a young man sent by the Rajah Muda Hassim to collect turtle eggs, which abound in this vicinity, especially on the larger island. The turtles are never molested, for fear of their deserting the spot; and their eggs, to the amount of five or six thousand, are collected every morning, and forwarded at intervals to Sarawak as articles of food" (*118* quoted in *106*:458). Again in 1842 Brooke visited Talang Talang Besar while in pursuit of pirates. He observed that the turtles came up as many as 100 a night in June and July and estimated that as many as 20,000 eggs might be laid nightly at the peak of the season (*151* quoted in *106*:458). Much as they do today, "watchers" marked with a flag the spot where each turtle nested and the following morning dug the soft-shelled eggs from the sand and crated them for shipment to Sambas, Pontianak, and other coastal markets.

Prior to this era, egg collection may be presumed to have been irregular because of the domination of the coast by pirates. After Brooke rid the area of these marauders, the collecting is reported to have been administered for some years by an enterprising Malay, apparently as a private monopoly. In 1875 the Rajah pre-empted the rights to turtle-egg collection and allotted them to one of the leading Malay chiefs of

61

Sarawak. Just prior to the Japanese invasion in 1942 the third Rajah Brooke bought control of the industry from the families that had inherited it from the chiefs, and set up the unique Turtle Trust Board under which it is administered today. During the war years the Japanese are said to have used the islands both as a source of meat and as a bombing target, but egg collection was regularized beginning in 1947 under the direction of the board. Production statistics, fragmentary since the beginning of the century and detailed since 1947, suggest the islands have consistently yielded 1,000,000 to 2,000,000 eggs a year. In the best years, 1934 and 1936, more than 3,000,000 eggs were harvested each year (*101*:7: 233-39; 8:504-14). There apparently are "class years" with turtles as with herring and sardines. The egg take of 2,065,000 in 1953 was the best of the early postwar years. A severe decline in the harvest followed. In 1956, for example, less than 30,000 eggs were harvested during the first six months. An exceptionally prolonged monsoon season was held partially responsible. By 1959, however, the cycle was at a new peak, with more than 1,000,000 eggs collected and marketable (*101*:9:277-78).

Turtles nest every month of the year on the islands off Sarawak, but nestings are fewest in February and reach a peak in August. The proportions between the three islands are remarkably constant. Talang Talang Besar accounts for about 50 per cent of the eggs deposited, Talang Talang Kechil 35 to 40 per cent, Setang Besar 10 per cent or less, the latter recently increased due to the abandonment of the leper colony there. The Talang Talang Besar beach, a sandspit approachable from the sea on two sides, may be the most intensively trafficked turtle beach in the world. An elaborate ceremony ("Semah") is annually held on the islands at the close of the monsoon season, and before the big summer rush comes, to frighten the spirits away so that the turtles will come up to lay (*101*:8:481-86; see also *100*).

Resident egg collectors live on each island. The eggs are offered for public sale, with the profits going to Malayan charities and the mosques. Exports to Singapore were once important, but the domestic Borneo market now apparently absorbs almost the entire production.

The killing of sea turtles is prohibited by Sarawak law. Recently experiments have been undertaken at the Talang Talang islands to improve the egg hatch and to study methods of rearing the young turtles so that they can be put into the sea in such a condition as to be able to resist attacks of the sharks and other fish that normally take the majority of them during the first days of their lives.

Tagging experiments by Harrisson and Hendrickson suggest that most of the females lay from 5 to 7 clusters of eggs during a season, a total of at least 500 eggs for each laying female. The 1,000,000 to 2,000,000 eggs that are taken from the beaches each year, then, would appear to represent the production of from 2,000 to 4,000 females. Since individual turtles do not appear to nest here more than once in three years and probably not more than once in four years, a population of perhaps 10,000 adult females may be involved in this community. In the course of the tagging activities every turtle that lays is logged, with the exact spot occupied on the beach recorded and mapped as a permanent record. Of the more than 1,500 turtles tagged in 1953 not one returned in the following two years, but early in 1956 they had begun showing up with regularity and repeating at intervals of ten to twelve days (106:490, 520).

It is hoped that tag returns will soon throw new light on the unsolved riddle of how far and where these Sarawak turtles go when they leave the nesting islands. No extensive aquatic vegetation has been discovered in the vicinity of the Sarawak coast, but the shoal waters of the reef-studded South China Sea, as around the Natoena Islands, undoubtedly contain extensive tracts of submarine pasture.

A young green turtle has never been caught in Sarawak waters, only adults being known to the Malay fishermen. Major William C Rogers, 1370th Photo-Mapping Group, United States Air Force, has told me that he has seen turtles in large numbers around Spratley, Sin Cowe, and North Danger islands in the South China Sea and that some of them haul up on the beaches there to lay. Turtlers from Viet Nam occasionally visit these islands, as they do the Paracels reefs (16° N.) (43). The Natoena group is also reported to support a breeding population.

THE PHILIPPINE TURTLE ISLANDS

The Philippine Turtle Islands are a group of seven hilly islets in the Sulu Sea where green turtles congregate in vast numbers during the nesting season. Prior to World War II they had been administered under a "gentlemen's agreement" by the British North Borneo Chartered Company, apparently in an effort to restrict smuggling activities. In 1947, following Philippine independence, they were formally handed over to the new Manila government. They have a permanent population of some 200 persons, currently ruled over by a descendant of the former sultans of Sulu, American-educated "Princess" Tarhata Kiram. They lie only twenty to thirty miles off the North Borneo port of Sandakan, while the Philippine provincial capital of Jolo under which they are administered is more than a hundred miles away. The light in the lighthouse of Taganak, largest and only permanently populated island of the group, sweeps the port of Sandakan.

Here, as in Sarawak, it is the turtle eggs that are prized, and the turning and killing of the reptiles on the beaches are prohibited. (The principal references on the Philippines are 62 and 223.) Egg collection is a well organized business, 15 pesos being paid to the Philippine government in 1953 for every 1,000 eggs taken. The government collected 22,000 pesos from this source in that year. There were said to be fourteen full-time egg collectors working on the islands, all recruited from Cagayan Sulu Island. Iron sounding rods are used to locate the nests. The months of May through September are the most productive, as in Sarawak, with the peak coming in August when the sea is calm. In 1953 egg collectors were said to be averaging 4,000 eggs a night on Taganak, nearly as many on Baguan, and 1,500 on Langaan. The take for the year exceeded 1,000,000 eggs. The other islets—Great Bakungan, Boaan, Lihiman, and Sibuang; an eighth, Little Bakungan, is on the British North Borneo side of the international boundary—more difficult to reach and less productive, were leased on a seasonal basis. Buyers came from outside, especially from Jolo, where turtle eggs bring 40 pesos per 1,000 on the market. Some are salted and dried. The principal prewar market was Sandakan, whence large numbers of eggs were forwarded to China, but the closing of the China trade and the cession to the Philippines has apparently interrupted this trade.

Under the prewar British administration these islands were said to have been more productive than today, but the records for the British period have not been found. The reported slaughter of female turtles by Japanese occupation forces during World War II is held partly responsible for their present depleted numbers, together with the rapid increase in the number of predatory dogs. Roots of coconut trees planted along the strand have made some beaches progressively unsuitable for nesting, as Carr has also observed occurring on Trinidad. These roots, exposed by wave erosion, in time form barriers which the female turtle is unable to negotiate to reach the high beach beyond. The British government used to clean and clear from the spawning grounds the many logs, coconut husks, and other obstructions cast ashore, but this practice has not been continued and some of the beaches are reported in danger of becoming unfit for nesting for this reason.

Turtles are found throughout Philippine waters and are occasionally harpooned in the open sea. Turtle meat is not taboo among the Filipinos. Thus, an account in 1668 of the natural history of the Vizayans by the Jesuit priest Alzina could describe the killing of turtle and the eating of its flesh by natives, observing its similarity to beef. The meat is even said to be especially favored among certain Muslim groups in the southern islands, where it is plentiful (2:tomo ii, cap. 17).* But the emphasis today is on eggs, as it was in Alzina's time, and it may be significant that Antonio Pigafetta, who kept the journal for Magellan's voyage, reported that the first Spaniards were offered palm wine and turtle eggs by the ruler of Cebu (19:33:149). The present-day prohibition against the slaughtering of egg-laying females in the Philippines is rationalized as a conservation measure, but it probably has cultural roots. A closed season every seventh year on egg taking, rotated among the islands, is reported to be in effect, but no management program exists comparable to that in Sarawak.

In addition to the Turtle Islands there is one islet (Bankawa) in the isolated San Miguel group, 120 miles north in the Sulu Sea, that is especially remarked on as a green-turtle nesting place. Eggs are also gathered at Cavili, Arena, Lumbuca, and Bancoran, which string out in a line to the northwest of the San Miguels. Marine turtles are also said to nest on Palawan.

Between the Philippine Turtle Islands and the British North Borneo mainland there are a number of small islands under North Borneo administration that are also frequented by nesting *Chelonia mydas*. From 100,000 to 250,000 eggs are said to be collected annually, the right being vested in the government and sold annually by tender. The most productive of these islands are Silingaan and Bakungan Kechil. While the months of July through October are the most productive, some nesting continues throughout the year. March is a closed month. For a time turtle fishing was permitted under license in these waters, but no turtle or turtle meat could be offered for public sale. A group of Cocos Islanders employed by a North Borneo tobacco estate held the license, which was withdrawn about five years ago (91:64).†

The evidence suggests that long-distance migrations may be less characteristic of this Sulu Sea breeding community

---

* Also personal correspondence, José S. Domantay, Chief, Division of Inland Fisheries, Manila, August 24, 1957.

† Also personal correspondence, E. J. H. Berwick, Director of Agriculture, Jesselton, British North Borneo, March 19, 1959.

than in the case of many others. Whether or not it has any connection with the Sarawak-South China Sea population is conjectural.

THE COAST OF AUSTRALIA AND THE GREAT BARRIER REEF

The first Europeans to go among the aborigines of northern Australia were much impressed by the turtling talents of these people who in many other ways seemed so very primitive. The coastal blacks still hunt *Chelonia mydas*, especially on the northern part of the Great Barrier Reef, in Torres Strait, and in the Gulf of Carpentaria, much as they did when Captain Cook visited them in 1770-71. Turtle, the principal meat among them, is favored because of its superior qualities over dugong flesh. Although the hawksbill also abounds in these waters, it is not commonly eaten. Green-turtle meat, cut into thin slices, boiled, stuck on skewers, and dried in the sun, provides the natives their traditional rations for long voyages (*239*:195-96; *139*; see also *98*:4:138). The turtles are taken at sea with harpoons having detachable, barbed wooden heads, the prey often being brought to gaff with the assistance of a suckerfish. Turtle eggs, too, are much esteemed, being collected by the native women at dawn to beat the scavenging dingoes, but the nesting females do not appear to be turned on the beaches. The turtle has apparently always played an important role in the life of the aborigines. It is frequently a totem, and has been a favorite subject for cave artists, as on Groote Eylandt. So important is it to them that the name of the green turtle is also applied to the season when it comes ashore to lay, from October through February.

The edible turtle ranges widely along the coasts of tropical Australia, and stray nests may undoubtedly be encountered wherever there are sand beaches. The principal concentration mentioned in the literature was formerly found on Capricorn Reef (23° 30' S.), a group of lovely coral cays astride the tropic at the southern end of the Great Barrier Reef. Here, on Heron Island and Northwest Islet, female greens originally hauled up by the thousands during each breeding season to deposit their eggs. Prior to 1930 at least two turtle-processing factories had operated on Northwest Islet and one on Heron, their product being shipped chiefly to markets in England. About twenty-five turtles seem to have been turned nightly during the season by the cannery workers (*153*:112-13). The gelatinous green calipee was dried, as were the flippers, while the bones were rendered to fertilizer.

The principal tinned product was a soup, flavored with pepper, onions, arrowroot, and other herbs. In the 1924-25 season, for example, 36,000 tins were shipped, the product of 1,600 turtles. When F. W. Moorhouse was on Heron Island during the 1929-30 season he observed a total of 1,755 "laying missions" between December 1 and February 16, although the previous year the cannery had "wiped out" the female population (*147*:18). This made it evident to him that individual females did not lay every year. The most turtles coming ashore in any one night was 51. No cannery operations seem to have been carried on in this season. At that time the turtles were said to have become so scarce that the company was forced to go to neighboring islands for part of its supply. He thought that only the fact that the first nests of the year were undisturbed (the company did not initiate work until December 1) had permitted operations to continue as long as they had. Apparently the females were turned on their backs as they came ashore without being given a chance to lay their eggs.

Cannery operations were closed down in the early 1930's and apparently were never resumed. Until 1954, however, slaughterhouses in Brisbane were receiving regular shipments of green turtles by rail from Gladstone, the port closest to Capricorn Reef (*141*). Some carcasses were being exported in the holds of ships transporting chilled beef to England, while other were consumed locally. Forty years of systematic exploitation, most observers agreed, had left the turtlery much depleted. Through the agency of the Great Barrier Reef Commission the green turtle was placed on the protected list by the government of Queensland in 1954, pending detailed investigation of its ecologic and economic status. Only the aborigines of the Torres Strait were permitted to take turtles or turtle eggs from the Great Barrier Reef area. Apparently this ban was later lifted, for in 1960 a Queensland group was urging Lusty's of London to set up a cannery there to process both kangaroo-tail and green-turtle soups. The supply of raw material was to be guaranteed, but high labor costs doomed the proposal.

As with most other centers of green-turtle populations, nothing is yet known of the migrations of these gifted navigators. It seems quite probable that the feeding grounds of the Capricorn turtles will turn out to be the northern waters of the Great Barrier Reef, as around the Turtle Islands (14° 40' S.) and Torres Strait where they are apparently especially abundant. Of the 1,300 greens tagged by Moorhouse thirty years ago at Heron Island, apparently not a single one was ever recovered, but this may have been because the tags were not securely attached.

Regarding the turtles on the north coast of Australia, we have the early testimony of Matthew Flinders, whose crew stowed forty-six aboard on one December night in 1802, of which the smallest weighed in excess of 250 pounds. The small island from which they were taken in the Gulf of Carpentaria he named Bountiful Island (16° 41' S., 139° 46' E.) because of its abundance of turtles. Without boats, the native Australians had apparently never reached such island breeding beaches, though itinerant Malay fishermen may have done so. Flinders thought that the laying season commenced in August and continued into the first months of the year, with each female laying several times. He was especially impressed by the high mortality rate among the young. "Were it not for the immense destruction made of these animals in the different stages of their existence," he wrote, "and that food must in the end fail, their fecundity is such that all the tropical seas and shores would scarcely afford room for them in a few years" (69:2:153-55).

In 1841 John Lort Stokes also found large numbers of turtles in the Gulf of Carpentaria as well as on the coasts to the west. He took thirty nesting greens and one hawksbill in four hours at a place he called Turtle Isles (20° S., 119' E.) off Point Hedlund, observing that "although we only took what was required for our own consumption, the number that could have been obtained here was enormous." Later, at Barrow Island in the Montebello Group on the Australian west coast (20° 45' S., 115° 30' W.), his crew loaded seven tons of the creatures "from the abundant supplies its shores provided" (200:2:176, 211).

Turtles are apparently still locally abundant on the remote and wild coast of Western Australia, but they are only casually mentioned in the literature. As late as 1951 a Sydney syndicate was canning turtle soup at Cossack Creek (20° 45' S.), not far from Barrow Island and Roebourne (31). About fifty green turtles were being processed each week, all of which were taken while feeding on the grass-covered reefs surrounding Flying Foam Islands, thirty miles to the south. The turtles were all "hand-picked," i.e., taken by swimmers who wrestled them onto their backs on the reef and received ten shillings for each so taken. There is no suggestion that these turtles nest in the vicinity, but neither is there any evidence as to where they may come from.

68

The green turtle, though known throughout the Pacific Islands, does not appear to be found in major concentrations anywhere among them. In most of the islands the taking of a turtle is an event sufficiently rare to call for a community celebration. There are indications, however, of a few more favored nesting beaches and feeding grounds and there were many more in the past.

A modest turtle fishery exists in the Hawaiian Islands, especially off the islands of Oahu, Molokai, and Maui. Between 1948 and 1958 official statistics indicate a catch averaging some 10,000 pounds a year, most of which finds its way to Honolulu restaurant tables. *Chelonia mydas,* however, is not known to nest anywhere on the main islands nor are specimens smaller than ten to fifteen inches in diameter ever taken by local fishermen.* Circumstantial evidence points to French Frigate Shoal (23° 45′ N.) and the other islands of the remote Leeward group as the home of most of the turtles found in Hawaiian waters. Of this string of tiny islands stretching northwest for more than 1,000 miles from Honolulu, only Midway and French Frigate Shoal are inhabited, the latter by a small Coast Guard detachment. All but Midway are in the Leeward Islands National Wildlife Refuge, so that the turtles are protected along with other wildlife. Even though there is no patrolling or supervision of these islands, they are so infrequently visited that violations must be extremely rare.

Most reports of green turtles in this area are of individuals basking on the shore during daylight hours, a behavior pattern that has been previously suggested as distinguishing the Indo-Pacific population from its Atlantic counterpart. While it is apparent that certain of the Hawaiian Leewards must be targets for nesting females during the fall of the year, the favored beaches do not seem to have been identified except in the case of French Frigate Shoal, where both nesting and basking populations have been reported. Dale Rice, who made numerous flights over the Leewards during 1957 and 1958 and spent time ashore on several of them observing the Hawaiian monk seal, reports having seen especially large concentrations of basking green turtles on Pearl and Hermes Reef, always on the same beaches, namely, on the north side of Southeast Island (usually twenty to fifty turtles) and a small bight on the south side of North Island (nor-

* Personal correspondence, Vernon Brock, Director of Division of Fish and Game, Territory of Hawaii, November 28, 1955; see also *160.*

mally ten to twenty turtles). Smaller numbers were present on Lisianski and Laysan atolls.* On more remote Midway juvenile greens are occasionally taken in the lagoon by skin-divers from the naval base, but adult turtles do not appear to haul out there today, undoubtedly because of the considerable human activity ashore.

The extent to which the Hawaiian Leewards may have been exploited for turtles in the past is conjectural. One account, at least, suggests that it was more than a casual matter. In the spring of 1882 a Japanese-chartered vessel for which we have a record took at least 390 turtles, including an undetermined number of hawksbills, in the Hawaiian Leewards beyond French Frigate Shoal. Of these 10 were taken at Midway, 28 at Pearl and Hermes Reef, 126 at Lisianski, 17 at Marco Reef, and 191 at Layson. Some were turned on the beaches and others harpooned at sea, but it is not clear whether those taken on land were turned during daytime hours or as they came ashore at night to make their nests. At Laysan, where 61 were turned within a few hours, a sign was found on shore that carried an appeal for passing ships not to take more turtles than needed. Their abundance at this time must have been such as to have encouraged waste. The visitors, apparently in sympathy with the recommendation, repainted the sign and placed it on a pole before leaving. At French Frigate Shoal, where they slaughtered a part of the catch and dried the meat in the sun, they must have taken more turtles. The account left to us only states that 47 gallons of turtle oil and 1,500 pounds of shell were added to their stocks there, along with bêche de mer, albatross down, and shark fins. The entire product of the voyage was eventually transshipped to Hong Kong, from where the turtle was sent on to England. (See *110;* the log was kept for six months by George Mansbridge, an employee of the Mitsubishi Company of Madagascar.)

It seems generally agreed that green turtles are much rarer today than they formerly were in Hawaiian waters. It is even possible to speculate that they once congregated on the beaches of Honolulu itself. Although, according to W. A. Bryan (*26:*299-300), the name is generally agreed to have been derived from a Hawaiian word, *hono,* meaning harbor (Honolulu, "quiet harbor"), one cannot resist pointing out that the Hawaiians know the green turtle by the almost identical term of *honu* and that beaches such as Waikiki might

* Personal correspondence, Dale Rice, Richmond, California, August 14, 1959, and Karl Kenyon, Sand Point Naval Air Station, Seattle, August 13, 1959; see also *117.*

have been attractive to nesting populations before man took over as the ecologic dominant.

There are scattered references to green turtles in the literature on the South Seas. At Pukapuka in the Tuamoto Group they are said to be not uncommonly taken on the beaches or seized in the lagoon by swimmers who throw a noose around their fore flipper and grapple them ashore with their hands. Today the taking of a turtle calls for a public feast, for by island law it is the property of all. Yet there is evidence even here of the disruption of a former more conservative relationship between man and nature in the statement of one native islander that "it is only in recent times, since people have taken eggs of turtles from the nest, that turtles have been dying out" (11:69-70, 105; 72). But it is difficult to reconcile this statement with other evidence that Pacific Islanders generally pay more attention to the eggs than to the meat of the turtle.

Mopelia, in the Society Group, is also locally renowned for its green turtles, which are said to come ashore to lay especially during the month of November (66; 129). Their numbers are apparently not large, for it is considered a good week when a dozen of them haul up on the beach. The natives here have been attempting to build up the depleted stock by protecting the young turtles and eggs against predators. Young turtles are raised in the lagoon for a year, then released. For every turtle a native raises and sets free he is allowed to send another to the Papeete market to be sold and credited to his account.

Another *Chelonia mydas* nesting center is Captain Cook's "Turtle Island," Vatoa, southernmost of the Fiji group. This may well be the home base for the greens that are reported to feed in substantial numbers off the Kermadec Islands (30° S.), midway between Fiji and New Zealand (159). The Kermadecs must be close to the southernmost limit of the species range and it is not surprising that it does not breed there. Generally the hawksbill seems to be more numerous and more important economically in Fijian waters than the green. The tiny island of Vomo, off the northwest coast of Viti Levu, was especially renowned in the last century for its tortoise shell. According to Charles Wilkes, the turtles were mostly taken between December and March, being kept in "pens" on the reef until needed (232:3:261).

Herold J. Wiens (230a:422-31) has recently reported several nineteenth-century references to localized nesting beaches in the central Pacific, some of which are not included in the front end leaf map. These include Rose Atoll (American Samoa), Palmerston Atoll, and Fanning Island. He also men-

71

tions the D'Entrecasteaux Reefs, at the north tip of New Caledonia, where William Billings, master of an American sailing vessel aground there in September, 1856, turned twenty-seven basking turtles in one morning without wetting his feet, and counted another eighteen asleep in only a few inches of water. One wonders whether they still haul up there today, and in what numbers.

In Micronesia the green turtle appears to be known everywhere, but it is more plentiful in the Carolines than in the Marshalls. Several atolls in the Central Carolines, east of Yap and south of Guam, have a special reputation as nesting centers, including Ulithi, Ifaluk, Gaferut, Olimarao, and Elato. "Uninhabited Olimarao is noted for its turtles and canoe loads of people from Lamotrek regularly go there to make copra and capture turtles and hunt their eggs during the laying season. Gaferut is said to be a favorite place for turtles but Faraulep islanders who own the island have not attempted to go there since 1950 when canoes started for the atoll but were caught in a storm resulting in the loss of around 12 lives including their chief" (216:5-6). On Ulithi and Ifaluk green turtles are said to be reserved for ranking clans and chiefs. On some of the islands the egg-gathering season was originally opened with elaborate and stylized rituals, but this is no longer the case. The turtles are here prized both for their meat and their eggs, being turned on the beaches and captured in the lagoons with the aid of harpoons or a noose, or even steered ashore by a powerful swimmer. During the Japanese occupation there was legislation against taking turtle eggs and nesting turtles, but enforcement was impractical. Similar restrictions have been imposed by the United States Trust Territory administration, apparently with no greater success. In several of the islands, as Palau, Ponape, Truk, Mokil, and Oroluk, natives recently have been reported to be raising young turtles in captivity until they are large enough to defend themselves against predators. In some cases this practice may have a native tradition behind it. However, it has more often been directed towards the hawksbill than the green variety.

THE WEST COAST OF MEXICO

Little is known about the geography and ecology of green turtles off the Pacific Coast of Mexico, but they are apparently relatively abundant from Acapulco northward to Bahía Vizcaíno, Baja California, and throughout the Gulf of California. They have been seen as far north as San Diego

Bay and Mission Bay. Good-sized nesting congregations have been reported on the Revillagigedo Islands, Socorro and Clarión, some 280 and 420 miles, respectively, off the southern tip of Baja California. They also go ashore in some numbers on selected beaches on the peninsula and on the mainland coast. William Beebe sighted fifty greens engaged in courtship activities when he arrived off the coast of isolated and uninhabited Clarión in May, 1937. Another morning he counted forty fresh turtle tracks on the crescent of white sand on the south side of the island. There is a striking photograph of this beach, criss-crossed as though by a large track-laying tank, in the chapter on the Clarión turtle sanctuary in his *Zaca Venture*. Neither he nor other visitors have made any reference to their commercial exploitation (*13*:281, 293; see also *23; 99; 192; 220*).

Sea turtles, at least in the past, also nested on the Tres Marías Islands off the Nayarit coast. Woodes Rogers, in 1709, described them as "of a very different sort from any I had ever seen, tho very good" (*180*:376). Edward Cooke, however, had no doubt that they were greens (*49a*:1:311). They were so abundant on the middle island when he was there in October, 1709, that two men could turn a hundred in a night. Later accounts, however, mention the Tres Marías as a retreat for hawksbills.

An indication of their former abundance on the Pacific side of Baja California is found in the report of the visit of the "Albatross" to San Bartolomé, or Turtle Bay (27° 45′ N.) in April, 1889, when a remarkable catch of 162 green turtles, many of "large size," was made in a single haul of a 600-foot-long seine (*210*:445-46). Half as many again were believed to have escaped from the seine before it could be beached. These may have been part of a breeding population, but more likely were feeding on the marine grasses of the shallow coastal lagoons. At about this time one Joseph P. Hale of San Francisco, who had also been active in the orchilla dyestuff trade, was operating a turtle cannery on a small island in Bahía Magdalena, some 250 miles to the south of Turtle Bay (*42*:408; *167*:213). In 1891 he was canning an "extract" of green turtle for export to England, as well as shipping live turtles to San Francisco. Fifteen years later the cannery was reported abandoned, but monthly shipments of live greens were still being made to San Francisco on vessels of the Pacific Coast Steamship Company (*154*:40,113). By this time concern was already being expressed that the unrestricted exploitation of this resource would eventually result in its destruction. Later, with the development of San Diego as a fishing and fish-canning center, Mexican turtles

Green turtles from Mexico awaiting slaughter outside a San Diego, California, turtle-soup cannery in 1920. Note cable rig for moving turtles from the pond.

(THE PACIFIC FISHERMAN, SEATTLE)

were shipped there in substantial numbers, in part by Japanese interests which held a turtle concession in Bahía Magdalena. In 1920 some 15,000 cases of turtle were reported canned in San Diego plants but restrictive Mexican legislation soon brought an end to the business (*16*:318-21). At this time the National City Commercial Company of San Diego (later the California-Pacific Sea Food Company) was described as the largest producer of green-turtle products in the United States (*6*:25).

Green turtles are still taken in substantial numbers by Baja California fishermen both on the gulf side and on the Pacific coast, but they are more frequently taken in nets or with harpoons than turned on beaches. In 1956 some 17,000 kilograms of fresh turtle and 5,300 kilograms of dried turtle were officially reported as produced by Baja California fishery cooperatives, most of the total coming from the southern part of the peninsula at such places as Laguna Ojo de Liebre (Scammon's Lagoon), Bahía San Bartolomé, Bahía de los Angeles, Bahía Magdalena (Puerto Alcatraz), and Bahía San Ignacio.* Although some were taken every month of the year, the largest numbers were reported for June, July, and August. Most of these turtles are trucked north over very poor roads to Ensenada, Tijuana, and Mexicali, where *hay caguama* signs on *cantinas* and butcher shops proclaim the news when turtle is in. (*Caguama,* Arawak term for the loggerhead turtle, is applied to the green in Baja California; elsewhere in Mexico *tortuga* is used.) Some are flown from

---

* Personal correspondence, Biologist Pedro Mercado S., México, D.F., January 2, 1958.

Scammon's Lagoon and Bahía Magdalena to the northern market cities. A turtle cannery, the property of Ruffo Hermanos' Empacadora Baja California of Ensenada, has been working in recent years at Bahía de Asunción (27° N.) between Scammon's and San Ignacio. The Ruffo concern has canned up to 100 tons of green-turtle soup in a season, according to Señor Ruffo, marketing the product almost exclusively on the peninsula. The turtles are taken in nets in the lagoons and estuaries along the desert coast during the summer months.[*]

For the aboriginal population of this parched desert land the sea turtle must have provided a most welcome dietary supplement. Homer Aschmann has estimated that turtle meat supplied 2 per cent of the total food intake of the Indians of the central desert of Baja California, exclusive of the eggs (4; he cites Baegert, Clavigero, and Longinos). Among the small remnant group of Seri of the Sonora coast at the head of the gulf turtles are still the most important single food resource, as they were when W J McGee was there in 1895. He estimated that there were 300 adult Seri at the time of his visit, a number that has since been further reduced. He wrote of the green turtle: "Its optimum habitat and breeding place would appear to be El Infiernillo [the channel that separates Tiburón Island from the Sonora mainland], whose sandy beaches are probably better adapted to egg laying and hatching [?] than any other part of the coast.

[*] Personal correspondence, David A. Henderson, University of Arizona, and Ernesto Ruffo, Ensenada.

"Black" turtles in a sand crawl at Kino, Sonora, Mexico. Caught around Tiburón Island in the Gulf of California, they are being held for shipment to Tijuana and Mexicali. (CARR)

Here it has been followed by the Seri; perhaps one-half of the aggregate life of the tribe is spent within easy reach of its feeding and breeding grounds, and tribesmen and turtles have entered into an inimical communality somewhat like that of the Siouan Indian and buffalo in older times" (*140*). McGee only saw the turtles being taken at sea by iron-tipped harpoons. His presumption of large-scale nesting is open to question. The Seri gorged themselves on raw turtle meat, he wrote, with "the impetuous fury of carnivorous beasts." His estimate that they obtained 25 per cent of their sustenance from this one source was, however, most certainly on the high side, as A. L. Kroeber also thought (*124:20*). W. B. Griffen has written a recent report on the Seri and the importance of the turtle in their culture (*93*). The Seri still harpoon them at night off the coast of their desert home on Tiburón Island, sometimes selling them to dealers at Puerto Kino to be trucked to Tijuana and Mexicali markets.

The green turtles of the Gulf of California, like those of the Cedar Keys section of the west coast of Florida, are apparently a half-grown, non-breeding congregation in which females are numerically predominant. These turtles are present in the warm waters of the gulf only in the summer months. Stomach examinations suggest that they feed on algae rather than the eel grass and turtle grass on which the Florida juveniles graze. To Archie Carr, who has recently made "a turtle reconnaissance" of the Mexican west coast (*36*), this all fits nicely into the world pattern of sea turtle natural history that is unfolding, in which half-grown green turtles seem commonly to live in places distant from both the feeding grounds on which the mature turtles spend most of their lives and the beaches to which they resort usually at three-year intervals to mate and nest. Where the baby turtles stay during the first years of their life no one knows.

The Mexican west coast *Chelonia mydas* has been observed by Carr to have a much darker head and flippers and a straighter-sided, more tent-shaped carapace than the Atlantic green turtle. It is either black or heavily blotched with sooty markings, the plastron clouded with blue. Early accounts also make mention of the differentiation between this turtle and those found elsewhere. Local fishermen call it *caguama prieta* ("black turtle"). Its southward range along the Pacific coast is uncertain.

On the mainland beaches of Mexico, from Cabo Corrientes southward, nests of both green and other species of sea turtle are frequently found. At Bahía Maruata, on a rugged and isolated stretch of the Michoacán coast southwest of Punta San Telmo, there is reported to be a localized nesting beach

A black turtle (tortuga prieta) at Kino Bay, Sonora, Mexico. Though structurally similar to the green turtle of the Atlantic and western Pacific, the population of the Gulf of California is generally melanistic, and the shell of the young female is slightly deeper. (CARR)

of major importance. James Peters (*169a*) observed the tracks of as many as 250 turtles in August, 1950, on a half-mile stretch of sand between two limestone spurs, with large numbers of turtles sculling offshore. This is apparently the same "Bay of Martaba" where, in November, 1704, Dampier's party anchored to water and, according to William Funnell, "found in a small river a great many green turtle, the best I ever tasted." The *Relación Geográfica* of Ixtlahuacán, Colima, September 12, 1778, mentions the multitude of turtle "accustomed to nest at San Telmo," which must be the same place. Significantly, its author remarks on the importance of the eggs as a food resource for the native population but makes no reference to the use of the flesh.

Donald Brand, who knows the area intimately, believes that "the Michoacán coast has the greatest number of egg-laying green turtles on the west coast of Mexico, with the Jalisco coast between Chamela and Cabo Corrientes coming next."*

*Personal communication, Donald Brand, Department of Geography, University of Texas, November 18, 1957; see also *22*.

Black turtle at La Paz, Baja California, the melanism characteristic of the population of the Gulf of California is not confined to the upper parts, but is found also on the belly, which is an even white or ivory in the Atlantic race. (CARR)

Black turtle at La Paz, Baja California, trussed for shipment. (CARR)

He reports having seen egg-laying turtles on the beaches from February through August. There is very little organized exploitation of either the meat or the eggs other than on a purely local basis. In the vicinity of resorts such as Acapulco, Manzanillo, Barra de Navidad, Puerto Vallarta, and San Blas there is a somewhat regular attempt to provide turtle meat for guests, while an occasional shipment of dried turtle may find its way to interior markets or to Tijuana. A government license is required, in theory, for the taking of live turtles. Brand suggests that a main reason why the isolated and inaccessible Michoacán coast is more frequented by green turtles is that "the Indians have discouraged any killing for meat or carapace," apparently to protect the egg supply. It is a commentary on the disparity between cultural attitudes towards conservation and conservation law that the taking of turtle eggs today is illegal in Mexico.

THE WEST COAST OF CENTRAL AND SOUTH AMERICA AND THE GALÁPAGOS

The green turtle does not appear to be particularly common on the Pacific coast of Central America. If it does breed there more than randomly it seems to have escaped the literature, although the nests of other types of sea turtles are common enough. Carr, for instance, states that during a four-year stay in Honduras he could find no definite evidence of *Chelonia mydas* nesting on the Pacific coast, although it was fairly abundant in the mangrove-bordered creeks in the Gulf of Fonseca from January to June (32:361). But 200 years ago there was clearly a major concentration of them on the uninhabited island of Coiba (Quibo), fifteen miles off the southwest coast of Panama. Dampier, who was there for five weeks in June and early July, 1685, wrote while there that his party "struck turtle every day, for they are now very plentiful" (53:1:234). This suggests harpooning in open water. But from the experience of George Anson, who rested his squadron at Coiba in December, 1741, after his sack of Paita, it is clear that the island beaches were alive at night with egg-laying females. His chronicler, Richard Walter, refers to "the prodigious quantity of turtle . . . [of which] we took what quantity we pleased with great facility," turning the females at night as they hauled up onto the beach (226:207-8). Enough were taken to provision them for a month at sea. Then, off the coast of Mexico, they ran into turtles again, "floating in great numbers on the surface of the water fast asleep." Anson's men fed on turtle meat continuously for four months without the least ill effect, "incontestible proof," Walter thought, of its superior dietary qualities. The turtles he described as being large, generally of about 200 pounds weight. While they may have been loggerheads or ridleys, it seems more likely from the context that they were greens.

The Englishman Colnett, at Coiba in February, 1794, complained of the difficulty of taking turtle there, although they were seen "in great abundance," apparently offshore. The surprising absence of turtles at Cocos Island he attributed to the great numbers of sharks that infested its waters (47:133). Occasional greens are said to be turned on the beaches of the Gulf of Panama and the Pearl Islands, or netted in adjacent Pacific waters, but most reaching the Panama City market today come from the Caribbean side of the isthmus. If Coiba still harbors the nesting turtles, it must be on the scattered beaches along the western side, for the Panamanian government's penal colonies are distributed along the entire eastern coastline, and there is much activity there. (Personal communication, April 20, 1959, from Alexander Wetmore of the Smithsonian Institution, who spent five weeks in Coiba in January and February, 1956, studying bird life. During that time he saw no turtles but was told that some usually came later to the beaches.) Were they at all abundant, they could hardly have escaped attention in the literature. It seems probable that the Coiba turtles have suffered the same fate as so many other turtle populations, pressed to the wall by the inadvertent interference of man.

What was probably a part of the same population was described by several seventeenth-century accounts as feeding in the shoal waters off Cape Blanco (Nicoya Peninsula), Costa Rica, but I have found no later accounts of turtle concentrations here. The nesting of green turtles on isolated Clipperton Island, some 1,600 miles to the west, has been reported, but there is no indication that more than scattered individuals are involved.

A second green-turtle "rookery" which was described more than two centuries ago and which still exists is that of the Galápagos Islands off Ecuador. That grand old pirate, Dampier, was in and about the Galápagos on several occasions and never failed to comment on the abundance of the greens that he observed grazing in the protected lagoons. They were, he wrote, "a sort of bastard type," larger and thicker shelled than the greens he had known elsewhere, their flesh less sweet (53:1:129-35). Although they must have done so in his day as they now do, Dampier did not observe them nesting on the Galápagos beaches. He believed that they nested on the adjacent mainland coast of Ecuador and at Isla La Plata (1° 10′ S.), a few miles off the Ecuador coast. "In the South

80

Seas . . . the Galápagos is the place where they live the biggest part of the year; yet they go from thence at their season over to the Main to lay their eggs; which is 100 leagues, the nearest place. Altho' multitudes of these Turtles go from their common places of feeding and abode to those laying places, yet they do not all go: And at the time when the Turtle resort to these places to lay their eggs they are accompanied with abundance of Fish, especially Sharks; the places which the Turtle then leave being at that time destitute of Fish, which follow the Turtle" (53:1:133). Dampier also noted that in the Galápagos, unlike most other places, the greens frequently came ashore during daylight hours to bask in the sun. Captain Woodes Rogers observed a similar behavior of green turtles on the west coast of Mexico (*180*:376). At Isla La Plata Dampier observed a substantial breeding population in the water in December, 1684, and he judged that they came from the Galápagos "for I had never seen any there before, tho' I had been there several times. This was their coupling time, which is much sooner here than in the West Indies. . . . Our strikers brought aboard every day more than we could eat" (53:1:182). On other occasions he had noted large numbers of very small green turtles "at Isla La Plata and other places thereabouts," which fed on moss and so were "very rank, but fat." There is a Bahía Tortuga on the mainland coast south of Esmeraldas, but according to local inhabitants whom I queried there in 1956 only occasional stray green turtles came ashore to lay either here or elsewhere on the Ecuador coast. Yet they may have done so in the more distant past. Recent archeologic work on the coast north of the Santa Elena Peninsula, for example, reveals very large concentrations of turtle remains in the earliest horizons (ca. 4,000 years ago), but much less in more recent times (Carlos Zevallos Menendez).

The Galápagos were named for their giant land tortoises rather than the sea turtles, and it was these that were especially exploited by whalers and sealers during the first half of the nineteenth century, both for their meat and for their oil. In an admirable study C. H. Townsend has estimated that more than 100,000 of them were slaughtered by American sailors and whalers alone in a period of thirty years after 1832 (*209*). The Americans, at least, apparently found them a more attractive provision than the green turtles. The latter, however, were not wanting. Captain Amasa Delano of Boston wrote of these islands (1817): "Green turtles are found here in great plenty; and they are the easiest procured of any place I ever visited in any part of the world" (57:381).

Four years earlier than Delano the crew of the United

States frigate *Essex* had turned more than thirty turtles, mostly above 300 pounds, on the Galápagos beaches. Captain David Porter thought them superior to any he had yet tasted, although they were described as having "a black, disagreeable appearance and smell," but shaped like green turtles, which they must have been. As good eating as they were, the land tortoise was even better. He observed that "The finest green turtle is no more to be compared to them in point of excellence than the coarsest beef is to the finest veal; and after once tasting the Gallipago tortoise, every other food fell greatly in our estimation" (*170*:146-51).

Captain Donald McLennan of the brig *Colonel Allen,* who was at the Galápagos in February, 1818, suggests much the same thing: "The green turtle abounds here as also the turpin or land tortoise, which is said by some to be the most delicate eating of the two. The fat of these is yellow and when melted down considered an excellent substitute for butter. I was informed that the Whaling Masters seldom came for turtle but always to hunt for Turpin and generally supply themselves with 500 or 600 at a time. They weigh from 150 to 300 pounds each, that is those which they consider fit for their purpose" (quoted in *225*:206). It was, however, "very troublesome and laborious" to get the tortoises on board because of their large size, and it was often more convenient to take the greens browsing in the lagoons. The latter, he wrote, could be procured in any quantity, being especially fat and fine eating because they fed on the leaves of the mangroves growing on the edges of the lagoons. Other observers, too, have suggested that mangrove leaves are a principal food of the Galápagos greens. James Colnett, the Englishman, who was at the Galápagos in June, 1794, observed, "I found the turtle far superior to any I had before tasted. Their food, as well as that of the land tortoise, consists principally of the bark and leaves of trees, particularly the mangrove, which makes them very fat. . . . The green turtle are extremely fat and would produce a large amount of oil." But he, too, thought the flesh of the land tortoise, especially the small ones, superior even to that of the greens; "in whatever way it was dressed," he wrote, "it was considered by all of us as the most delicious food we had ever tasted" (*47*:56, 157).

It would be interesting to know whether other Englishmen who visited the Galápagos held views similar to the Americans' on the relative merits of tortoise and sea-turtle steak. Perhaps they did not. Young Charles Darwin, there on the H.M.S. *Beagle* in 1835, found the meat of the land tortoise but "indifferent food," although he noted that the young ones made a "capital soup" (*54*:341).

The population of green turtles here seems not to have been so badly decimated as was that of the tortoises, perhaps because the English played a back seat to the Americans on the Galápagos in the whaling era. William Beebe was presumably referring to greens when he wrote of the islands a century later, "Sea turtle abound. On a launch trip to Duncan Island from Seymour Bay we passed thru a school of hundreds floating lazily with the current and covering over a mile of sea surface. Nearly all the steep beaches that we found formed nesting places for these turtles, the beach at James Bay being particularly adapted for this purpose" (12:237).

Recent visitors to the Galápagos report that the greens still congregate in considerable numbers during the early months of the year at three or four localized beaches and adjacent lagoons. Tortuga Bay, on the south side of Albemarle Island, is said to be the center of the largest assemblage, its beaches being strewn with their skeletons left by Ecuadorean oil collectors.*

It seems almost certain that the Galápagos beaches are the home of the green turtles that are frequently encountered in the waters of the cold Humboldt Current off the coast of Peru, for they apparently do not nest anywhere on this desert littoral. Green turtles, however, are frequently taken by fishermen in nets at least as far south as Pisco (14° S.), and sizeable piles of turtle shells are found on most of the desert beaches of northern Peru.

* Personal communication, Robert I. Bowman, San Francisco State College.

An extraordinary custom and a curious parallel

THE USE OF SUCKERFISH IN TURTLING

Reports of the extraordinary custom of tropical fisherfolk of using suckerfish or remora (*Echeneis* spp.) for taking both green and hawksbill turtles have taxed the credulity of many eminent biologists. However, the exhaustive researches of Gudger (1919), more recently supplemented by the observations of De Sola (1932), Hornell (1950), Grottanelli (1955), and others leave no doubt as to their authenticity. As remarkable as the technique itself is the geographical distribution of this strange method of taking sea turtles, with the aid of what amounts to a semi-domesticated fish. The custom is recorded for such widely separated areas as the Caribbean, the east coast of Africa, northern Australia, 84 and the South China Sea, but not in intervening areas.

A curious, oblong sucking-disk, a modification of the first dorsal fin, enables these extraordinary fishes to affix themselves securely to the bottoms of ships and to the bodies of whales, sharks, and other large marine creatures as well as turtles, thereby to be carried about without effort on their own part. Among the Ancients there were many extravagant legends about them, especially regarding their ability to halt ships.

Everywhere that turtling is practiced with these strange fish, the details of the technique are remarkably similar. The suckerfish, with a long line secured to the base of its tail, is tethered to a fishing boat, often a dugout or canoe. Whenever the fishermen believe that a turtle may be near, the suckerfish is released; and, wearied of its confinement, it dashes off in the direction toward which it is pointed, its line trailing behind it. When a turtle is found, the "hunter fish" by some instinct attaches itself firmly to the carapace by its powerful dorsal suction cup, and remains fastened while both are drawn to the boat or canoe. Skillful and patient handling of the light line is required, for the turtle usually dives, exerting all its strength to escape. But the adhesive power of a large suckerfish is marvelous, and only when raised above the water does it normally release its hold.

The first account of the use of the suckerfish in turtling is that of Columbus, who on his second voyage observed the practice in 1494 among the islands of the Jardinella de la Reina on the south coast of Cuba. The remora, he thought, attached itself to the turtle for no other reason than that it provided a large solid mass that served well as a resting place from where short excursions could be made in search of food. The account in his journal, edited by his son Ferdinand, was published in 1501 by Peter Martyr and later by Oviedo y Valdés (*163*:21-22), who noted that the same method was also used by the Arawak for taking manatee. E. W. Gudger, after a painstaking and admirably exhaustive review of the literature, was convinced that the use of the remora for taking turtles must have vanished from the Antilles with the aboriginal population (*96*). However, in 1932 De Sola established beyond doubt that hawksbill turtles, at least, are still taken in this ingenious manner by native fishermen in the same Jardinella de la Reina waters where the practice was observed by Columbus more than 450 years ago (*60*). He himself observed a pair of remora (Spanish, *reverso, pegador;* Arawak, *guiacan*), one 31 inches long and the other 35 inches long, being employed by turtlers at Matanzas on the north coast of Cuba, and reported that his father had seen it used only a few years earlier at Puerto Colombia (Savanilla), Colombia, a few miles from Barranquilla, by a small group of "Indians" from the town of Tuburá. The earlier, second-hand account of the use of suckerfish at La Guaira, Venezuela, by Lady Anne Brassey (1885) has thus gained additional significance (quoted in 96:453). Remora fishing may well yet be practiced on the north coast of South America, though Raymond Gilmore quotes one informant who specifically denies its existence in Venezuela (80:414). It is unknown to any of the Colombian anthropologists I have queried regarding the matter.

On the other side of the world aborigines of the Torres Strait area of Australia, especially at Thursday Island, make extensive use of the suckerfish (*gafu*) to take both green and hawksbill turtles, as was documented in detail by A. C. Haddon half a century ago (98:4:163-65; 5:44-46, 67, 92; 6:41-42). Remora fishing for turtle has also been recorded among Chinese fishermen at Singapore and in the South China Sea (27 in 96:454-55) and, earlier, among the nomadic Bajau fisherfolk of Makassar (*134*:89).

The use of suckerfish for turtling is especially prevalent off the east coast of equatorial Africa. Dampier, who never missed a turtle story, seems to have been the first to have recorded the practice, though only from hearsay (53:2:322). It attracted the attention of several rather incredulous Europeans who traveled in this area during the last century, including Commerson, Salt, and Sparmann. For Zanzibar Hornell has quoted an 1883 account by Holmwood on how the suckerfish is caught there while young and undergoes a special training regimen before being used in fishing (*111*:35). It is kept in a canoe partially filled with sea water and fed pieces of meat and fish until it becomes used to the man who feeds it and tolerant of being handled. When it reaches a weight of two or three pounds it is considered strong enough for use and is taken out for trial. The fish soon learns what is required of it.

Recently both Grottanelli (95:324) and Copley (50: 1950:37) have given detailed accounts of the modern usage of *Echeneis* (*chazo, khasa*) among the Bajun peoples, a Bantu fisherfolk who occupy the string of low, desert islands that lie astride the equator in southern Somaliland and northern Kenya. The technique has also been reported for Zanzibar, Mozambique, the Comores, and Madagascar (Nosy Bé).

Copley's description of suckerfish turtling among the Kenya Bajuni is extraordinary enough to bear extensive quotation:

Sucker fishes are caught by anchoring the boat in the lagoon and fishing with a line baited with cut fish bait. It is stated that in some areas they cannot be caught on anything but cooked bait. When caught the fish are tied with a line through the gill opening and mouth, the line is made fast to the boat and the fish adhere to the bottom of the boat. When about 10 have been caught the boat proceeds to the turtle fishing grounds. From long use the best places are known which are usually the ends of off shore banks with depths of 4 to 10 fathoms, and are weed covered.

On arrival the sucker fish are removed from the bottom of the boat and the line taken from their mouths, and a 30 to 50 fathom line is made fast to their tails. The fish then attach themselves again to the side of the boat, which is anchored. They leave the boat by themselves when they scent a large animal such as a turtle, shark, dugong or large grouper. The line is payed out by the fisherman until the sucker fish attaches itself to its prey, when the anchor is taken up and the boat is towed by the turtle until it is played out, when it is pulled in and gaffed. As the turtle leaves the water the sucker fish lets go and attaches itself to the bottom of the boat again. Sucker fish always attach themselves to the *dorsal* surface of the prey, usually on the back of the turtle behind the neck: once attached they never let go. Hence it is not popular when they attach to a large grouper (tewa) as this fish invariably dives and enters a hole in the rocks and, as it cannot be pulled up, the line has to be cut. Sharks are also a nuisance, because the sucker fish will attach to them, and a large shark may exhaust the sucker fish until it lets go. A shark will occasionally kill the sucker fish if the hold is not near enough to the back of the head, by turning and biting it.

Whenever a turtle is aware of the approaching sucker fish it will always endeavor to escape, even before contact is made. Fishermen state that a sucker fish never misses, but the line is sometimes exhausted before contact is made.

Some sucker fish are lazy and do not leave the boat when a turtle is sighted, in which case the fisherman will whip it with a small stick he takes for this purpose or bite its tail— they usually then go and do their work! A good sucker fish will catch about two turtles per day before being too tired, when it is rested for 36 hours. At nights they are untied and placed in a loose mesh basket alongside and fed. A fairly good day's catch for the boat will be six to seven turtle.

In a personal communication to the author, May 7, 1956, T. E. Allfrey, Senior Assistant Fish Warden, Game Department, Malindi, Kenya, has added some additional notes to this remarkable account:

Although the sucker fish will detach themselves from the bottom of the boat if they sight a turtle, or other large animal, as stated in the [Copley] report, the fisherman usually spots the turtle first and pulls the sucker fish off the bottom of the boat and throws them into the sea in the direction of the turtle. The fishermen in this industry are well acquainted with areas of turtle grass and it is usual for them to anchor over the beds, detach a sucker fish which they throw into the water and which then searches the bottom for turtles. Most are caught in this manner. When a sucker fish attaches itself to a turtle it is the aim of the fisherman to endeavor to get at least one other, and preferably two or more sucker fish on the same turtle. From experience it has been found that if the fisherman succeeds in getting three sucker fish on a turtle it never escapes. It he gets two sucker fish on it the turtle has about a 20 per cent chance of getting away; if the turtle has to be played out with only one sucker fish on it, it has about a 75 per cent chance of escaping. When the sucker fish have attached themselves to the turtle the anchor of the boat is taken up and the turtle played until it sounds on the bottom vertically beneath the boat, when a grapnel on a stout line is run down the light line attached to the tail of the sucker fish and jerked into the turtle, which is then heaved up and brought on board.

From experience in capturing Green Turtle, both by harpooning and by netting, I am in no doubt of the opinion that this odd method of capture is by far the most successful. . . . During the year 1954 approximately a thousand turtles were exported from Kenya, nearly all of them captured by the sucker fish method.

It is noteworthy that wherever it is so employed for taking turtle the suckerfish is reported to be treated with extreme respect by the native fishermen. The relationship is apparently somewhat similar to that between a hunter and his retriever dog. It is stroked, spoken to with soft words of encouragement or thanks, and fed special food. When it fails to perform, it is verbally scolded, given the lash, or even bitten. Whether in Australia, East Africa, or the Caribbean, the natives seem to believe that this remarkable fish well understands human speech. In East Africa, indeed, there is said to be a special vocabulary that is employed in addressing the *Echeneis*.

In view of the singularity of the trait, which has been likened to cormorant fishing, and the pan-tropic distribution of both marine turtles and suckerfish, it is tempting to believe that we are dealing here with a single culture complex that has been diffused across the Indian Ocean, perhaps from Indonesia westward to Africa, along with such other traits as the outrigger canoe (cf. 94:157). Even a trans-atlantic (or transpacific?) transfer cannot be entirely ruled out, though the more conventional ethnological view will doubtless hold the Arawak practice to be an independent invention (e.g., Sven Lovén, 137:400). Raymond Decary has even attributed the distribution of this trait along both sides of the Mozambique Channel to the simple convergence of ideas, explained by the similarity of reasoning of native peoples who are good observers. He sees the remora-green-turtle complex as a warning to ethnologists with a tendency to deduce the existence of ancient contacts in the face of cultural similarities among distant people (55:97). But to others such a position will seem unnecessarily conservative. We will probably never have sufficient information to completely resolve this enigma, which is but part of the larger question of pre-Columbian culture transfers between the Old World and the New World. Certainly no opportunity should be lost to record further details connected with this ingenious manner of taking turtles, wherever it survives.

THE RIVER TURTLE OF THE ORINOCO AND AMAZON

In both its behavior pattern and the history of its wantonly wasteful exploitation by man, the socially spawning South American river turtle, *Podocnemis expansa*, bears a striking resemblance to the green turtle. Like the latter, the adult females of the river turtle, which weigh from 25 to 125 pounds, migrate long distances each year during low water to nest *en masse* on certain favored sand bars and islands in the great rivers of tropical South America. Incredible multitudes of these "cattle" of the Amazon and Orinoco formerly assembled on localized and well-known beaches at certain seasons, the noise of their shells striking against each other in the rush being reported audible for great distances. The easy availability of the eggs, of the newly hatched young, and of adult females made *Podocnemis expansa* a staff of life for the river people. The turtles seem to have been held by the native population to be used as needed. Vásquez de Espinosa, in a second-hand account of Pedro de Ursua's journey down the Amazon in 1560, describes a large settlement named Arimocoa in which more than 4,000 river turtles were found kept in enclosures by the native population. They were said to be "a great staple" for river tribes living as far up as the Guayapoco. Vásquez also makes reference to the great abundance of turtle eggs on the Orinoco and on the lower Río Cauca in Colombia (221:67, 339, 412). Raymond M. Gilmore (80) and Manuel Vicente Ramírez (175) offer the most recent and accessible summaries of the literature on *Podocnemis expansa*. There are other socially congregating river turtles in Asia. William Tandy described a sandbank in the Ava River, Burma, from which eggs and live turtles were taken "sufficient to supply a great part of the kingdom" (*202*:155).

For at least three centuries these river turtles of South America have been under heavy pressure from man both for their eggs and, to a lesser degree, for their oil and meat, until today this once abundant resource has been all but exterminated over much of its former range. As with the sea turtle, the newly hatched baby river turtles are the targets of predatory birds, animals, and fishes so that scarcely 1 in 500 is believed to survive to adulthood. Protective legislation in both Brazil and Venezuela from time to time has been aimed at bringing back the river turtles, but until recently enforcement has been almost completely ineffective.

The nineteenth-century naturalists who traveled these waters, such as Humboldt, Bates, Spruce, and Agassiz, invariably were impressed by the role of the *Podocnemis expansa* in the local economy, as earlier Spanish and Portuguese had been. There are many sixteenth and seventeenth century accounts from the Amazon. One, in 1639, observed that the river folk "collect turtles in such abundance that there is not an enclosure which does not contain upwards of a hundred. Thus, these people never know what hunger is, for one turtle suffices to satisfy the largest family" (*1*:69-70). Though the meat was highly prized, greater importance was attached to the eggs, which were collected during the daytime hours and piled in heaps as much as twenty feet high that resembled, according to one account, "stacks of cannon balls such as are seen at Navy yards." Prior to the introduction of kerosene *manteiga da tartaruga* (*manteca de tortuga*) was used on a large scale for lamps, while as an edible oil it was much favored as a substitute for butter or lard, despite its fishy taste. In the early part of the nineteenth century several million eggs were said to have been broken in the Amazon valley yearly for the manufacture of *manteiga*, with considerable quantities of it being shipped south to Bahia and Rio de Janeiro (*46*:286). Daniel Kidder, in 1845, wrote that the industry was already in decline "owing to the inroads made upon the turtle race, and also to the advance of civilization" (*120*:2:288). The eggs were rendered into oil by crushing them with the bare feet in a canoe and mixing them with water. On exposure to the sun the oil accumulated on the surface, to be skimmed off, heated in pots, and clarified, when it assumed the appearance of melted butter.

Emilio Goeldi, writing in the 1890's, documented the de-

Podocnemis expansa being carried off to waiting boats on the Orinoco for shipment downstream to consuming centers.
(VENEZUELAN EMBASSY, WASHINGTON, D.C.)

cline of the turtle industry in the Amazon and ascribed the near extinction of this most useful reptile to its unregulated exploitation. Thirty years earlier it had been of major economic importance. Persecuted on its favored beaches, the animal had been forced to nest on narrower down-river strands more subject to flooding and hence less tenable. Between the mouth of the Amazon and the Rio Negro, where it had once been superabundant, Goeldi wrote that no single locality then harbored a group of more than 15 individuals! But there were still beaches along the Madeira where they congregated in such numbers as to impede the passage of canoes. The turning of live turtles was by then prohibited, while it was required that at least one third of the eggs be left on the beaches. A government inspector was established at each beach during the nesting season, but most of them were corrupt and the efficacy of the regulations was doubtful (*81*:733-45; for a current account with illustrations see *222*).

The Venezuelan government recently has been taking strong measures to control the threatened disappearance of

this species from the upper Orinoco and to re-establish it as a primary food resource. Padre Gumilla, in his *Orinoco ilustrado,* published in 1745, had compared the number of turtles in the river with the grains of sand on its shores and asserted that these animals would have been so numerous as to block the movement of boats if it were not for the enormous consumption of turtle and turtle eggs by both men and jaguars (97:1:331-36). Humboldt, a half century later, gave considerable attention to the Orinoco turtles. He reported an annual production of 5,000 jars of oil from three beaches then under exploitation on the river above its junction with the Río Apure. This would have required 330,000 separate nestings if one jar represented the product of 5,000 eggs, as he estimated. The German geographer thought that the yield must have been even greater during the eighteenth century and urged that egg harvesting be terminated for three or four years to permit the population to re-establish itself (*113:2: 184-95*).

According to a recent and detailed report by the Natural Resources Division of the Venezuelan Ministry of Agriculture there are today four major nesting beaches on the Orinoco (Isla Pararuma, Playa del Medio, Playa Blanca, Cabullarito) between Ciudad Bolívar and the Atures rapids, and at least five lesser ones (*175*). Since 1946 the concessions for their exploitation have been under the control of the Ministry. The extent of the depletion of the *Podocnemis expansa* stock is indicated by the statistics. In the peak year 1950 a total of 51,000 individual nestings were recorded on the four principal beaches, which, calculating at 75 eggs to the nest, yielded 3.8 million eggs. The Playa del Medio alone accounted for nearly half of this figure. Between 8,000 and 16,000 live turtles have been taken annually in recent years by the concessionaires, who operate under strict controls. Eggs are no longer taken. The river boats that come to the beaches to load turtle are especially numerous during Holy Week, for then the meat is in special demand.

The average weight of the nesting turtle is about 70 pounds on the Orinoco, apparently much less than it was in former times when specimens weighing up to 200 pounds were reported. Females, which alone come out onto the beaches at night, are both much larger and much more numerous than the males. As with the tropical green turtle, the females apparently lay only once every four or more years, apparently always returning by instinct to the same beaches. Of some 40,000 Orinoco turtles that were marked for study in 1946, the first did not begin to reappear on the beach where they were tagged until 1950.

It should be of interest to students of marine resources, concerned with the future of the green turtle, that transplants of young *Podocnemis expansa* have been successfully made in recent years into Lake Valencia in the Andean highlands north of the Orinoco and west of Caracas. The species is reported both growing well and nesting there, aided by artificial nesting beaches that have been constructed on some of the islands of the lake.

The parallel between the histories of *Podocnemis expansa* and *Chelonia mydas* is clear. Among the native Indian populations of the rain forest, living in approximate harmony with their environment and with probable community regulations and taboos against the killing of nesting females, the river turtle was a renewable resource managed on a sustained yield basis. Today it is relatively rare, large-scale nestings being confined to the more remote headwaters of the Amazon and the Orinoco. Once again it has been Western Man, concerned with maximizing short-run (lifetime) returns rather than with living within and being a part of his natural environment, who has upset the equilibrium. But there is yet good reason for hope that scientific management and international cooperation may right affairs if they are immediatley instituted and pursued with sufficient vigor and imagination.

The future of the edible green turtle in an expanding world

The highly localized feeding and nesting grounds of the green turtle, its clumsiness in matters to do with procreation, and its sheer size have made it an easy target for man. It first attracted attention as an antiscorbutic to supplement the monotonous shipboard fare of the buccaneers. Later it became a staple, either fresh or salted, of the slaves and persons of the lower classes in the tropical colonies. Eventually it reached the tables of the rich and of royalty, until green-turtle flesh and green-turtle soup became a symbol of status, particularly in England. The prestige thus attached to it, coupled with the growing food requirements of the tropical world, has helped sustain the market demand for *Chelonia mydas* until today the green turtle is in trouble. In Carr's words "the people are expanding too fast for the turtle," and growing populations, faster ships, and better refrigeration will pose grave threats to its survival in the near future in many areas. It has long since been swept from the Bermudas, the Bahamas, Florida, the Dry Tortugas, and the Cayman

94

Female green turtle nesting at Tortuguero, Costa Rica.
(CONNER)

Islands in the New World and from the islands of the Indian Ocean along the sailing routes to Bengal and Malacca. One can scarcely imagine a more clear-cut example of how man, in his folly and ignorance, has found it within his power permanently to impair a highly prized and desirable resource that, wisely managed, might contribute significantly to his own welfare.

The recognition of the vulnerability of the green turtle to man dates at least as far back as 1620, when the Bermuda legislature passed a conservation law in its behalf. Nearly 200 years ago Oliver Goldsmith wrote that "at present, from the great appetite that man has discovered for this animal, they are not only thinned in their numbers, but are grown more shy" (*82*:676). In discussing the green turtle the *Nouveau dictionnaire d'histoire naturelle* (1804) observed that in view of the avid demand for both the meat and the eggs, it was not surprising that the animals were becoming scarce in the very places that they had originally been most abundant (*158*:248). This situation, it observed, had led the philanthropist Martin Moncamps to propose the establishment in the Seychelles, under the authority of the French government, of some turtle reserves (*parcs à tortues*) "where both males and females might be protected for better reproduction." These reserves, it was emphasized, would contrast with the turtle "crawls" of Jamaica and elsewhere, "which only hasten the depopulation of the turtle by making them more readily available to the luxury trade of London." But there is no evidence that anything ever came of this enlightened proposal.

In later years most of those who have been concerned with the green turtle have warned of the dire consequences to be expected from the animal's continued uncontrolled exploitation. Yet the pace has slackened but little. It was being proposed in a London journal only ninety years ago that tinned turtle meat, long the cherished luxury of the rich, might provide an almost unlimited source of low-cost meat for the workers of industrial Europe "were the business but properly organized" (*46*:289).

Until the past five or ten years there has been a notable lack of protective legislation covering the green turtle in the face of the almost universal belief that the population of the species is rather rapidly diminishing. Almost simultaneously in the Caribbean, in the Seychelles, in Queensland, and in the Pacific Islands there has been an awakening to the fact that rapid action may be necessary to salvage the green-turtle resource. In Sarawak thousands of turtle eggs are now being put down in special hatcheries so that the young may be put

95

into the sea in such a condition that they may better resist the attacks of sharks and other predators that normally take the majority of them in the first few minutes of their lives. Similar experiments are being made in the Pacific Trust Territory, in the Seychelles, and in Costa Rica. Tagging programs have been proposed elsewhere so that the mysteries of the green turtle's migrations and life history may be better understood. Archie Carr, who is spearheading the turtle conservation program in the Caribbean, has expressed the situation succinctly but with optimism: "It is not often that we are offered a set of circumstances so promising; a one-item feeder with its pastures undamaged, vast in extent and used by no other animal; a species attuned to building and thriving in dense populations and yet flexible enough to proliferate and scatter in dilute colonies; above all, a depleted species, the cause of whose depletion is clear and surely possible to remedy. There is a skeletal breeding stock and the best of remaining nesting shores are the least cluttered by man. Group action by governments concerned would surely save Chelonia and build unity and strength in the Caribbean by raising the yield of the sea to the people around it. In the field of live-resource management it is not often that you can hope for so much" (33:19).

The green-turtle problem has been attracting much attention during the last few years and steps are beginning to be taken in several areas to save this fabled creature, so beloved of epicures and gourmets, from going the way of the passenger pigeon, the heath hen, and the great auk. A case in point is the Brotherhood of the Green Turtle, an informal layman's organization that was founded in New York City in the spring of 1959, inspired by Professor Carr's delightfully readable book of Caribbean wanderings and turtle lore, *The Windward Road*. The club, sparkplugged by a New York publishers' representative named Joshua B. Powers, has established a non-profit subsidiary known as the Caribbean Conservation Corporation, of which Carr is the technical director, supported by a small field staff comprised mostly of graduate students in biology. Its first project is the provision of free stock from a hatchery at Tortuguero, Costa Rica, to any agency able to ensure protection for any beach formerly used for nesting green turtles and since abandoned. In the summer of 1960 some 20,000 baby greens were hatched. About one fourth of these were released off Tortuguero, the remainder shipped by air express to Florida, Puerto Rico, the Cayman Islands, and other Caribbean points just like day-old chicks. The hatchlings are released at dark, in small groups, a few hundred yards offshore to circumvent predator loss insofar as possible.

A portion of an aerial strip photo of the Tortuguero, Costa Rica, area where the Ministry of Agriculture has set aside five miles of beach for Carr's conservation and research work. This area is one of the few nesting grounds left to turtles in the western Caribbean.

The Tortuguero story

97

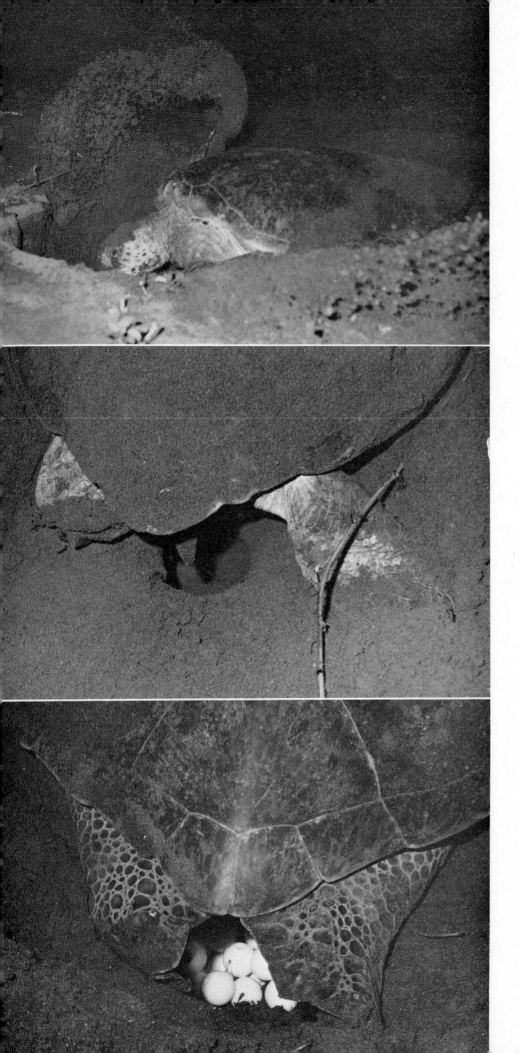

Tortuguero green turtle digging the concealing basin in which she rests while laying her eggs. Note sand flying from right flipper.

Completing the digging of the egg cavity—the nest proper.

The end of the laying process—a hundred or so eggs are ready to be covered.

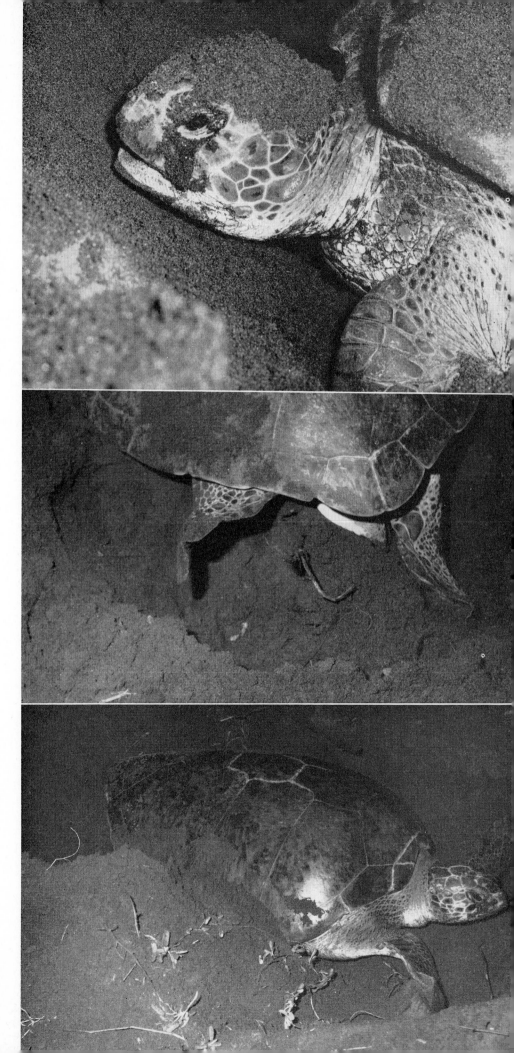

Green turtle nesting. The open mouth and the tears which have caked the sand under her eye do not indicate labor pains. Although the tears serve to keep the sand out of the eyes, it has recently been learned by Dr. Schmidt-Nielson of Duke University and his collaborators that tears of sea birds and turtles serve the important function of ridding the body of excess salt taken in with food and water.

After having laid her eggs, she fills, covers, and packs the nest hole. She then completely covers and conceals the body pit and nest site (below).

Turned on her back after she had finished nesting the night before, this turtle is now being dragged to the scales for weighing.

Tagging. Of some 2,000 turtles tagged during the past six years, there have been 61 tag recoveries from all parts of the Western Caribbean. The only extra-Caribbean return was from the Gulf side of the Yucatán Peninsula at Campeche.

A series of measurements are taken each time a turtle is tagged.

Weighing. The average weight for the mature female is 250 pounds; the maximum is about 350 pounds.

Her dignity restored, the turtle is returning to the sea to help trace the travels of her kind if her tag should one day be sent in for the reward its inscription offers in Spanish and in English.

Digging out turtle eggs for the hatchery. During the first 36 hours after they have been laid, the eggs can be handled without injury. Thereafter, they become more sensitive to shock and the embryos may die if the egg is turned upside down.

Leo Martinez, the only year-round employee of the Caribbean Conservation Corporation, which is staffed by volunteers, takes the eggs by dugout canoe to the hatchery.

At the hatchery the eggs are buried in the sand. Each transplanted nest of about 100 eggs is enclosed within a wire circle.

An unprotected nest that has met the usual fate—destruction by dogs or wild animals.

Individual circles of hardware cloth facilitate collection of the hatchlings and recording of hatching percentages. The fenced-in nest-patch keeps out dogs and wandering female turtles that would push over the nest circles.

Baby turtles being removed from the circular fence placed around each nest in the hatchery. During the 1961 season there were 300 such fenced-in nests, all surrounded by a high fence of chicken wire to keep out predators.

The baby sea turtles are tended in the nursery where they are kept until shipping time in 20 wooden tanks to which water is pumped from the sea out in front.

Two of the tanks in which hatchlings are held prior to being released or sent to conservation agencies about the Caribbean. Left, hawksbills; right, green turtles.

Twenty per cent of each batch of baby turtles sent away for release are tagged.

Tagged green turtle hatchlings; note plastic disk on hind foot.

Tagged hatchlings ready for shipment.

The big Navy Grumman coming in after the 1961 crop of turtle hatchlings to be distributed among 17 localities about the Caribbean.

Part of the shipment of turtles brought by Navy plane from Tortuguero in an effort to re-establish the green turtle at the island of St. Lucia.

Releasing a part of the season's crop of little green turtles out in front of the nesting beach at Tortuguero.

Green turtle being butchered at Tortuguero. Although commercial exploitation of turtles is now prohibited by the government on the 5-mile strip where the research camp is located, a few turtles are killed each season for the use of the village, where turtle meat has always been one of the few reliable sources of protein.

A year-old green turtle from the Tortuguero hatchery, reared in the laboratory at the University of Florida. At this age, when the turtles weigh between four and eight pounds, they change from the juvenile carnivorous habit to a completely herbivorous diet. The grazing habit is, of course, the attribute that makes them the most important reptile in the world. (CARR)

Crate of hatchery green turtles from Costa Rica sent to Florida for restocking former green-turtle grounds on the lower East coast. (CARR)

It is hoped that survivors will be imprinted by the conditions of their first immersion in the sea and go back to the site of introduction at nesting time, as some fish do. But even if their genes send them back to Tortuguero to nest, Professor Carr notes, the protection will have been achieved and there will be a net gain for the green turtle (21).

There is some evidence that the green turtle has best held its own against man in those areas where the eating of turtle flesh is held repugnant and the eggs alone are prized, as in the Malay world and much of Buddhist Southeast Asia. Hendrickson has recently argued, in his study of the breeding populations of Malaya and Sarawak, that the key to the rational management of the species lies in the fact that the exploitation for eggs has a much less adverse effect than the slaughter of adult green turtles (106:525-29). He points out that the species is adapted to sustain enormous losses in the first part of its life and that this loss might be represented instead by a 95-per-cent egg harvest if the turtles hatched from the remaining 5 per cent could be reasonably sure of surviving the first few days of life. A hatchery program is proposed much as has been initiated in Costa Rica, involving the transportation of egg clutches to protected spots, the removal of predators, wire enclosures to prevent newly hatched turtles from wandering into the sea, and tanks in which the young turtles may live for perhaps a week or until the yolk supply which they carry with them from the egg is exhausted.

It is argued that the average mature green turtle yields about 150 pounds of edible meat and that this is about the weight of the lifetime egg production of a female, assuming 600 eggs for each of three egg-laying seasons (the number may well be twice this). But as most of the eggs could be utilized without removing the producing unit, there seems no doubt that exploitation for eggs would yield the larger nutritional product. Hendrickson suggests that no luxury demand should be allowed to produce a net nutritional loss in the protein-poor areas of the tropics, particularly when past history indicates that the form of exploitation necessary to supply the luxury obliterates the industry concerned after a time. If green-turtle soup is to continue to be made available to the epicures, he argues, its price must go up and a significant share of the higher profits obtained from its sale must be plowed back into intensive management programs for the remaining turtle populations. In an egg-orientated turtle industry, he suggests, the biologically exhausted females might be called upon to provide at least a minimal supply of flesh and fat.

Convincing and logical as this argument is, it nevertheless seems improbable that it will govern the green-turtle economy

of the future any more than it has in the past. The extraordinary role which cultural attitudes and preferences have
played in the history of exploitation of the species has been
demonstrated. All men do not like turtle meat and many
even find it repugnant on religious or esthetic grounds. Others find the gritty, soft-shelled eggs equally unattractive; they
are the size and shape of ping-pong balls and have an al-
bumen that does not coagulate but remains watery after cook-
ing. A rational, conservative system of harvesting the sea will
have to consider cultural attitudes along with biological facts.
In the case of *Chelonia mydas,* a species peculiarly vulnerable to man's activities, the lesson of history is already writ
large. Now amateur "skin-divers" must be added to its list of
enemies. Should present exploitation practices and human
population trends prevail, its days as an economically significant source of protein food for the tropics are undoubtedly
numbered. Yet the very persistence of this giant reptile to date
in the face of such tremendous odds is in itself something of
a tribute to the vigor of the species, the vastness of the Seven
Seas, and the importance of cultural differentiation among
110   men.

Bibliography

1. Acuña, Fray Cristoval de. 1859. A new discovery of the great river of Amazons, 1639 [1641]. *In* Clements R. Markham (*ed.*), Expeditions into the valley of the Amazons. Hakluyt Soc. London. 24:42-142.

2. Alzina, Francisco Ygnacio. 1668. Historia natural del sitio, fertilidad, y calidad de las islas e yndios Vizcayas. MS no. 478. Museo Naval, Madrid.

3. Anonymous. 1835. Communication on Ascension Island. J London Geogr. Soc. 5:243-63.

4. Aschmann, H. Homer. 1959. The demography and ecology of the central desert of Baja California. Ibero-Americana (Berkeley and Los Angeles). Vol. 42.

5. Audubon, Maria R. 1897. Audubon and his journals. New York. 2 vols.

6. Avarett, W. A. 1920. Lower California green turtle fishery. Pacific Fisherman (Seattle) 18(7):24:25.

7. Ayyangar, S. Ramaswami. 1922. Notes on the fauna and fishery industries of the Laccadive Islands. Madras Fisheries Bull. 15:45-69.

8. Baalbergen, C. B. 1938. Kustvisscherijn Bengkalis. Med. Ver. Gezaghebbers B.B. in Ned. Indië 48:41-47.

9. Babcock, H. L. 1937. The sea-turtles of the Bermuda Islands, with a survey of the present state of the turtle fishing industry. Proc. Zool. Soc. London (Series A) 107:595-601.

10. Bates, Henry Walter. 1892. The naturalist on the river Amazons, a record of adventures, habits of animals, sketches of Brazilian and Indian life and aspects of nature under the equator during eleven years of travel. 5th ed. London. 2 vols.

11. Beaglehole, Ernest and Pearl. 1938. Ethnology of Pukapuka. Bernice P. Bishop Mus. Bull. 150. Honolulu.

12. Beebe, William. 1924. Galápagos, world's end. New York.

13. ———. 1938. Zaca venture. New York.

14. Beeton, Isabella. 1909. Mrs. Beeton's book of household management; a complete cookery book. London.

15. Bell, Charles Napier, 1899. Tangewera; life and adventures among gentle savages. London.

16. Bell, P. L. and H. Bentley MacKenzie. 1923. The Mexican west coast and Lower California; a commercial and industrial survey, U. S. Dept. Comm., Spec. Agent Ser., no. 220. Washington.

17. Benjamins, H. D. and Joh. F. Snellman (eds.). 1917. Encyclopaedie van Nederlandsche West Indië. Leiden.

17a. Berchet, Guglielmo (ed.). 1893. Fonti italiani per la storia della scoperta del nuovo mondo. Rome. Parte III, Vol. II.

18. Bernardin de St. Piere, J. H. 1800. A voyage to the isle of France, the isle of Bourbon and the cape of Good Hope. London.

19. Blair, Emma Helen and James A. Robertson. 1903-09. History of the Philippine Islands, 1493-1803. Cleveland. 53 vols.

20. Boulenger, George A. 1912. A vertebrate fauna of the Malay Peninsula. London.

21. Bowen J. David. 1960. To save the green turtle. Américas 12 (12):14-17.

22. Brand, Donald D. 1957-58. Coastal study of southwest Mexico. Dept. Geogr., Univ. Texas, Austin (processed). 2 vols.

23. Brattstrom, Bayard H. 1955. Notes on the herpetology of the Revillagigedo Islands, Mexico. Amer. Midland Naturalist 54:219-29.

24. Breton, Raymond. 1665. Dictionnaire français-caraïbe. In Charles de Rochefort, Histoire naturelle et morale des îles Antilles de l'Amérique. Rotterdam. 2:652-80.

25. Bruce, James. 1790. Select specimens in natural history collected in travels to discover the source of the Nile. . . . Edinburgh. 5 vols.

26. Bryan, W. A. 1915. Natural history of Hawaii. Honolulu.

27. Bullen, Frank G. 1904. Denizens of the deep. Chicago.

28. Burkhill, I. H. 1935. A dictionary of the economic products of the Malay Peninsula. London. 2 vols.

29. Burma. 1916. Burma Gazetteer. Rangoon. Vol. 4, Bassein District.

30. Cadamosto, Alvise. 1937. Cadamosto, a Venetian in the service of Prince Henry the Navigator. Hakluyt Soc. London. New s., vol. 80.

31. Caldwell, Norman W. 1951. The turtle hunters. Walkabout (Sydney) 17(7):29-32.

32. Carr, Archie. 1952. The handbook of turtles. Cornell Univ. Press, Ithaca, N.Y.

33. ———. 1954. The passing of the fleet. Bull. Am. Inst. Biol. Sci. 4:17-19.

34. ———. 1956. The windward road. New York.

35. ———. 1957. Notes on the zoogeography of the Atlantic sea turtles of the genus Lepidochelys. Rev. Biol. Tropical (San José, C. R.) 5:45-61.

36. ———. 1961. Pacific turtle problem. Nat. Hist. 70:64-71.

37. ——— and David Caldwell. 1956. The ecology and migrations of sea turtles, I; Results of field work in Florida, 1955. Am. Mus. Novitates no. 1793.

38. —— and Leonard Giovannoli. 1957. The ecology and migrations of sea turtles, II; Results of field work in Costa Rica, 1955. Am. Mus. Novitates no. 1835.

39. —— and Robert M. Ingle. 1959. The green turtle (Chelonia mydas mydas) in Florida. Bull. Marine Sci. Gulf and Caribbean 9:315-20.

40. —— and Larry Ogren. 1960. The ecology and migrations of sea turtles, IV; the green turtle in the Caribbean Sea. Bull. Amer. Mus. Nat. Hist. 121:1-48.

41. Catesby, Mark. 1731-43. The natural history of Carolina, Florida, and the Bahama Islands. London. 2 vols.

42. Chamberlain, E. K. 1949. United States interests in Lower California. Ph. D. thesis, Univ. California, Berkeley.

43. Chang, H. T. 1948. The vegetation of the Paracels Islands. Sunyatsenia 7:75-88.

44. Chapin, James. 1946. Wideawake fair invaded. Nat. Hist. 55:313-19.

45. Chevalier, August. 1935. Les îles du Cap Vert: Flor de l'archpel. Rev. Intern. Agr. Tropical y Botan. Appliquée 15: 733-1090.

46. Cochrane, William. 1872. Turtle. The Food Journal (London) 3:255-58, 286-90.

47. Colnett, James. 1798. A voyage to the South Pacific and round Cape Horn. London.

48. Cook, Captain James. 1824. An account of a voyage toward the South Pole and around the world, 1772-75. In Robert Kerr (ed.), A general history and collection of voyages and travels. London. Vol. 15.

49. ——. 1955. Journal of Captain James Cook; the voyage of the Endeavor, I, 1768-71. Hakluyt Soc. London. Extra Series no. 34.

49a. Cooke, Edward. 1712. A voyage to the South Sea and round the world. . . . London. 2 vols.

50. Copley, Hugh. 1951-55. Review of Kenya fisheries, 1950; 1951; 1952; 1953; 1954. Government Printer, Nairobi.

51. Covarrubias, Miguel. 1937. The island of Bali. New York.

52. Crawfurd, John. 1830. Journal of an embassy . . . to the coasts of Siam and Cochin China. 2nd ed. London. 2 vols.

53. Dampier, Captain William. 1906. Dampier's voyages [1679-1701], John Masefield, ed. New York. 2 vols.

54. Darwin, Charles R. 1933. Diary of the voyage of the HMS Beagle, edited from the manuscript by Nora Barlow. New York.

55. Decary, Raymond. 1950. La faune malagache, son rôle dans les croyances et les usages indigènes. Paris.

56. DeGaury, Gerald. 1957. A note on Masira Island. Geogr. J. 123:499-502.

57. Delano, Captain Amasa. 1817. A narrative of voyages and travels in the northern and southern hemispheres. Boston.

58. Dennys, N. B. 1894. A descriptive dictionary of British Malaya. London.

59. Deraniyagala, P. E. P. 1953. A colored atlas of some vertebrates from Ceylon. Colombo. Vol. 2.

60. De Sola, C. Ralph. 1932. Observations on the use of the sucking-fish or remora, Echeneis naucrates, for catching turtles in Cuba and Colombian waters. Copeia (2):45-52.

61. Díaz del Castillo, Bernal. 1908. The conquest of New Spain. Hakluyt Soc. London. New s., vol. 23.

62. Domantay, José S. 1952-53. The turtle fisheries of the Turtle Islands. Bull. Fisheries Soc. Philippines 3-4:3-27.

63. Doran, Edwin B. 1953. A physical and cultural geography of the Cayman Islands. Ph. D. thesis, Univ. California, Berkeley.

64. Drake, Sir Francis. 1854. The world encompassed [1628]. Hakluyt Soc. London. Vol. 16.

65. Edwards, Clinton. 1957. Quintana Roo, Mexico's empty quarter. Dept. Geogr. Univ. California, Berkeley (processed).

66. Eggleston, George T. 1953. Tahiti; voyage through Paradise. New York.

67. Fauvel, A. A. 1909. Unpublished documents on history of the Seychelles Islands anterior to 1810. Mahé, Seychelles.

68. Fernández, León (comp.). 1881-1907. Colección de documentos para la historia de Costa Rica. San José, C. R. 10 vols.

69. Flinders, Matthew. 1814. A voyage to Terra Australis . . . in the years 1801, 1802, and 1803. London. 2 vols.

70. Fontoura da Costa, A. (ed.). 1939. Cartas das ilhas de Cabo Verde de Valentín Fernándes, 1506-08. Lisbon.

71. Forrest, Thomas. 1779. A voyage to New Guinea and the Moluccas . . . during the years 1774, 1775, 1776. Dublin.

72. Frisbie, Robert D. 1929. Mrs. Turtle lays her eggs. Atlantic Monthly 143:462-66.

73. Fryer, John. 1909. A new account of East India and Persia, 1672-81. Hakluyt Soc. London. New s., vol. 19.

74. Fryke, Christopher. 1929. A relation of a voyage made to the East Indies, 1680-88. In E. Ernest Fayle (ed.), Voyages to the East Indies. Seafarers' Library, London.

75. Gardiner, J. Stanley. 1906. The fauna and geography of the Maldive and Laccadive archipelagoes . . . being the account of the work carried on and the collections made by an expedition during the years 1899 and 1900. Cambridge Univ. Press. 2 vols.

76. Garman, Samuel. 1884. The reptiles of Bermuda. U.S. Nat. Mus. Bull. 25:285-303.

77. Gentleman's Magazine, The (London). 1753-54. 23:441, 489; 24:337.

78. Gibson-Hill, C. A. 1950. Papers on the fauna of the Cocos-Keeling Islands. Bull. Raffles Mus. (Singapore), no. 20.

79. Gill, Mrs. David. 1878. Six months on Ascension. London.

80. Gilmore, Raymond M. 1950. Fauna and ethnozoology of South America. In Julian H. Steward (ed.), Handbook of South American Indians. Smithsonian Inst., Bur. Am. Ethnology Bull. 143. Washington. 6:345-464.

81. Goeldi, Emilio A. 1906. Chelonias do Brazil. Bol. Mus. Goeldi de Hist. Nat. e Ethnographía (Pará) 4:699-756. In part a condensation of Joao Martins da Silva Coutinho, Sobre as tartarugas do amazonas, Bul. Mensual de la Soc. Imperiale Zoologique d'Acclimatación, April, 1868.

82. Goldsmith, Oliver. 1825. A history of the earth and animated nature [ca. 1770]. London.

83. Grandidier, Alfred and Guillaume (eds.). 1903-05. Collection des ouvrages anciens concernant Madagascar. Paris. 5 vols.

84. Grandidier, Guillaume. 1910. Les tortues de mer à Madagascar. Rev. Madagascar (Tananarive) 12:298-308.

85. Great Britain. 1842. House of Lords Sessional Papers. London. Accounts and Papers no. 27, vol. 14.

86. ————. 1889, 1893, 1898. Public Record Office. Calendar of State Papers, Colonial Series, American and West Indies. London. Vols. 7, 9, 11.

114

87. ———. 1926-32. Colonial Office. Reports, St. Helena. London.
88. ———. 1948, 1956, 1958, 1960. Colonial Office. Reports, Seychelles. London.
89. ———. 1950-51. Colonial Office. Reports, Sarawak. London.
90. ———. 1953. Colonial Office. Report on the Mauritius-Seychelles fisheries survey, 1948-49. Fishery Publ., London. Vol. 1, no. 3.
91. ———. 1954. Colonial Office. Report, North Borneo. London.
92. ———. 1955-56. Reports, Cayman Islands. London.
93. Griffen, W. B. 1959. Notes on the Seri Indian culture, Sonora, Mexico. Univ. Florida Press (Latin Am. Monographs 10), Gainesville.
94. Grottanelli, Vinigi L. 1947. Asiatic influences on Somali culture. Ethnos (4):157.
95. ———. 1955. Pescatori dell'oceano Indiano. Rome.
96. Gudger, E. W. 1919. The use of the sucking fish for catching fish and turtle: Studies in Echeneis or Remora. Am. Naturalist 53:289-311, 446-67, 515-25.
97. Gumilla, Padre Joseph. 1745. Orinoco ilustrado. Madrid. 2 vols.
98. Haddon, A. C. 1904-12. Reports on the Cambridge Anthropological Expedition to Torres Strait. London. Vols. 4-6.
99. Hanna, C. Dallas. 1926. Expedition to the Revillagigedo Islands, Mexico, in 1925. Proc. Calif. Acad. Sci. ser. 4, 15:1-113.
100. Harrisson, Tom. 1950. The Sarawak Turtle Islands "Semah." J. Roy. Asiatic Soc., Malayan Branch 23:105-26.
101. ———. 1951-59. The edible green turtle (Chelonia mydas) in Borneo. Sarawak Mus. J. (Kuching) 5(3):593-96; 6(4): 126-28; 6(6):633-40; 7(7):233-39, (8):504-14; 8(11):481-86; (12):772-74; 9(13-14):277-78.
102. Hartwig, G. 1860. The sea and its living wonders (transl. from 4th German ed.). London.
103. Hawkins, John. 1878. The Hawkins voyages, Clements R. Markham, ed. Hakluyt Soc. London. Vol. 57.
104. Hayward, Abraham. 1899. The art of dining. New York.
105. Heller, Edmund. 1903. Papers from the Hopkins-Stanford Galápagos Expedition, 1898-99, XIV, Reptiles. Proc. Wash. Acad. Sci. 5:39-98.
106. Hendrickson, John. 1958. The green sea turtle, *Chelonia mydas* (Linn.), in Malaya and Sarawak. Proc. Zool. Soc. London 130(Ser. A):445-535.
107. Holmwood, Frederick. 1884. On the employment of the remora by native fishermen on the east coast of Africa. Proc. Zool. Soc. London (1884):411-13.
108. Hongkong Naturalist. 1931. 2:82-83.
109. Hornell, James. 1927. The turtle fisheries of the Seychelles Islands. H. M. Stationery Office, London.
110. ——— (ed.). 1934. Log of the Schooner "Ada" on a fishing cruise in the North Pacific, 1882. Mariner's Mirror 20:426-37.
111. ———. 1950. Fishing in many waters. Cambridge Univ. Press.
112. Hübener, Th. 1898. Die Inseln Mona und Monita. Globus 74:368-72.
113. Humboldt, Alexander von. 1852. Personal narrative of travels to the equinoctial regions of America during the years 1799-1804. London. 3 vols.

114. Hummelinck, Wagenarr. 1940. Studies on the fauna of Curaçao, Aruba, Bonaire and the Venezuelan islands, I. Utrecht.

115. Ingle, R. M. and F. H. Walton Smith. 1949. Sea turtles and the turtle industry of the West Indies, Florida and the Gulf of Mexico. Spec. Publ., Marine Laboratory, Univ. Miami, in cooperation with the Caribbean Research Council. Miami, Florida.

116. Kenya (Colony and Protectorate). 1951-57. Review of Kenya fisheries. Nairobi.

117. Kenyon, Karl W. and Dale W. Rice. 1959. Life history of the Hawaiian monk seal. Pacific Sci. 13:215-52.

118. Keppel, Henry. 1847. The expedition to Borneo of the HMS Dido. London.

119. Keuning, J. (ed.). 1942, 1947. De Tweede Schipvaart der Nederlanders naar Oost-Indië onder Jacob Cornelisz van Neck en Wybrant, Warwijck, 1598-1600. Linschoten Ver., 's Gravenhage. Vols. 46, 50.

120. Kidder, Daniel P. 1845. Sketches of residence and travels in Brazil. Philadelphia. 2 vols.

121. King, William. 1907. The voyage made to the Bay of Mexico by M. William King Captaine . . . from Ratcliffe the 26 of January 1592. In Hakluyt's Voyages, 7:154-56. Everyman's Library, London.

122. Knight, E. F. 1895. Cruise of the "Alerte." London.

123. Kooper, W. J. C. 1936. The soup turtle of Java. Nederlandsch Indië-Oud en Nieuw (Amsterdam), Yearbook, 1936, pp. 181-84.

124. Kroeber, A. L. 1931. The Seri. Southwest Mus. Papers, no. 6. Los Angeles.

125. Labat, J. B. 1724. Nouveaux voyages du Père Labat aux îles de l'Amérique. The Hague. 2 vols.

126. Lacépède, Comte de. 1847. Histoire naturelle (new ed.). Paris. Vol. 1.

127. Laet, Johannes de. 1931-37. Het Laerlyck Verhael van Johannes de Laet de Verrichtinghen der Goeetroyeerde West-Indische Campagnie (1624-44). Linschoten Ver., 's Gravenhage. Vols. 34 (1931), 35 (1932), 37 (1934), 40 (1937).

128. Larousse, Pierre (ed.). 1876. Grand dictionnaire universel du XIXᵉ siècle. Paris. Vol. 15.

129. Legand, Michel. 1950. Contribution a l'étude des méthodes de pêche dans les territoires français du Pacifique Sud. J. Soc. Océanistes 6:141-84.

130. Leguat, François. 1891. The voyage of François Leguat of Bresse to Rodríguez, Mauritius, Java and the Cape of Good Hope [1691]. Hakluyt Soc. London. Vols. 82, 83.

131. Le Poulain, F. 1941. Note sur les tortues de mer du golfe de Siam. Annexe, pp. 215-18, to René Bourret, Les tortues de l'Indochine. Inst. Océanographique de l'Indochine, Station Maritime de Cauda (Nhatrang). Publ. 38.

132. Lewis, C. Bernard. 1940. The Cayman Islands and marine turtle. Bull. Inst. of Jamaica Sci. Ser. 2:56-65.

133. Life. May 12, 1958.

134. Lindeman, Moritz. 1880. Die Seefischereien, ihre Gebiete, Betriebe und Erträge in den Jahren 1869-78. Petermann's Mitt. Vol. 13, Erganzungheft 60.

135. Linschoten, Jan Huygen van. 1934. Itinerario van Jan Huygen van Linschoten, 1579-1592, III [1596]. Linschoten Vereeniging 's Gravenhage. Vol. 39.

136. Long, Edward. 1774. The history of Jamaica. London.

137. Lovén, Sven. 1924. Über die Wurzeln der Tainischen (Arawak) Kultur. Göteborg.
138. Lowe, R. Percy. 1911. A naturalist on desert islands. London.
139. McCarthy, Frederick D. 1955. Aboriginal turtle hunters. Australian Mus. Mag. 11:283-88.
140. McGee, W J. 1895-96. The Seri Indians. Bur. Am. Ethnology, Washington. Ann. Report no. 17, Part I, pp. 1-344.
141. McNeill, Frank. 1955. Saving the green turtle of the Great Barrier Reef. Australian Mus. Mag. 11:278-82.
142. Man, Edward H. 1932. The Andaman Islanders [1885]. 2nd ed. London.
143. Marchand, Etienne. 1807. Voyage autour du monde pendant les années 1790, 1791 et 1792. Paris.
144. Martyr, Peter. 1912. De Orbe Novo, the eight Decades of Peter Martyr d'Anghera, tranl. and ed. by F. A. McNutt. New York and London. 2 vols.
145. México. 1952. Archivo General de la Nación. El libro de la tasaciones de pueblos de la Nueva España, siglo XVI. México, D.F.
146. Mondolfi, Edgardo. 1955. Anotaciones sobre la biología de tres Quelonias de los llanos de Venezuela. Mem. Soc. Ciéncias Nat. "La Salle" (Caracas), 15:177-83.
147. Moorhouse, F. W. 1933. Notes on the green turtle (*Chelonia mydas*). Great Barrier Reef Committee Reports. Brisbane. Vol. 4, part 1.
148. Morison, Samuel Eliot. 1942. Admiral of the ocean sea; a life of Christopher Columbus. Boston.
149. Mowbray, L. S. and David K. Caldwell. 1958. First record of the ridley turtle from Bermuda, with notes on other sea turtles and the turtle fishery in the islands. Copeia (2): 147-48.
150. Mulville, Dan. 1961. Trade winds and turtles. Toronto.
151. Mundy, C. Rodney. 1848. Narrative of events in Borneo and Celebes. London.
152. Murphy, Robert Cushman. 1925. Bird Islands of Peru. New York.
153. Napier, S. Elliott. 1928. On the Great Barrier Reef. Sydney.
154. Nelson, Edward W. 1921. Lower California and its natural resources. Nat. Acad. Sci. Memoirs. Vol. 16.
155. New York Times. August 24, 1939; September 17, 1959.
156. Nicoll, J. J. 1909. Three voyages of a naturalist. 2nd ed. London.
157. Notes and Queries (High Wycombe, England, etc.). 1855, 1884. 1st ser., 12:168-69; 6th ser., 9:114-15.
158. Nouveau dictionnaire d'histoire naturelle. 1904. Paris. 22:242-71 ("Tortue").
159. Oliver, R. B. 1910. Notes on reptiles and mammals in the Kermadec Islands. Trans. New Zealand Inst. 43:535-39.
160. Oliver, James A. and Charles E. Shaw. 1953. The amphibians and reptiles of the Hawaiian Islands. Zoologica 38:65-95.
161. Ommanney, F. D. 1949. The shoals of Capricorn. London.
162. Oviedo y Valdés, Gonzalo Fernández de. 1851-55. Historia general y natural de las Indias occidentales. Madrid. 4 vols.
163. ————. 1959. Natural history of the West Indies, transl. by Sterling A. Stoudemire. Univ. No. Carolina Press Chapel Hill.
164. Ozanne, J. A. 1936. Coconuts and creoles. London.
165. Parsons, James J. 1954. English-speaking settlement in the

western Caribbean. Yearbook, Assoc. Pac. Coast Geogr. 16:3-16.

166. ———. 1956. San Andrés and Providencia, English-speaking islands in the western Caribbean. Univ. Calif. Publ. Geogr. 12:1-75.

167. Pendergast, Thomas F. 1942. Forgotten pioneers: Irish leaders in early California. San Francisco.

168. Penyapol, Commander Amporn, R.T.N. 1958. A preliminary study of the sea turtles in the Gulf of Siam. Nat. Hist. Bull. Siam Soc. 17:23-36.

169. Petermann's Mitteilungen. 1879. 25:362.

169a. Peters, James. 1956-57. The eggs (turtle) and I. The Biologist 39:21-24.

169b. Ponce, Fray Alonso. 1873. Relación breve y verdedura de algunas cosas de las muchas que suciederen al Fray Alonso Ponce en las provincias de Nueva España. . . . Madrid. Vol. 2.

170. Porter, David. 1822. Journal of a cruise made to the Pacific Ocean by Captain David Porter in the U.S. frigate "Essex" in the years 1812, 1813 and 1814. 2nd ed. New York.

171. Pyrard, François. 1887-90. The voyage of François Pyrard to the East Indies, the Maldives, the Moluccas and Brazil [1611]. Hakluyt Soc. London. Vols. 76, 77, 80.

172. Quesada, Alejandro. 1952. La pesca. Estructura Económica y Social de México (Nacional Financiera, S.A.). México, D.F.

173. Radcliffe-Brown, A. D. 1933. The Andaman Islanders. Cambridge Univ. Press.

174. Raffald, (Mrs.) Elizabeth. 1808. The experienced English housekeeper, for the use and ease of ladies, house-keepers, cooks, etc. . . . 13th ed. London.

175. Ramírez, Manuel Vicente. 1956. Estudio biológico de la tortuga "arraú" del Orinoco, Venezuela. Agricultor Venezolano 21(190):44-63.

176. Raven, H. C. 1946. Predators eating turtle eggs in the East Indies. Copeia (1):48.

177. Roberts, Captain George. 1726. The four years voyages of Capt. George Roberts, being a series of uncommon events. . . . London.

178. Robinson, W. 1874. Report on the Laccadive Islands [1848]. Madras.

179. Rochefort, Cèsar de. 1666. The history of the Caribby Islands [1658]. London. 2 vols.

180. Rogers, Captain Woodes. 1824. Voyage round the world by Captain Woodes Rogers and Stephen Courtney in 1708-11. In Robert Kerr (ed.), A general history and collection of voyages and travels. London. Vol. 10.

181. Roze, J. A. 1955. Las tortugas maritimas de Venezuela. Rev. Pecuaria (Caracas), no. 240.

182. Salt, Henry. 1814. Voyage to Abyssinia and travels in the interior of that country, executed under the order of the British government in the years 1809 and 1810. London.

183. Schaw, Janet. 1939. Journal of a lady of quality, being the narrative of a journey from Scotland to the West Indies, North Carolina and Portugal in the years 1774 to 1776. New Haven.

184. Schmidt, Karl P. 1945. Problems in the distribution of the marine turtles. Marine Life (New York) 1(3):7-10.

185. Scott, Sir Robert. 1961. Limuria: the lesser dependencies of Mauritius. Oxford Univ. Press, London.

186. Shafer, Edward H. and B. F. Wallacker. 1957-58. Local tribute products of the T'ang dynasty. J. Oriental Studies 4:225.

187. Sherman, W. T. 1899. Memoirs. New York. Vol. 1.

188. Simmonds, Peter Lund. 1859. The curiosities of food, or the dainties and delicacies of different nations obtained from the animal kingdom. London.

189. ———. 1883. The commercial products of the sea. 2nd ed. London.

190. ———. 1885. Animal food resources of different nations. London.

191. Simoons, Frederick J. 1961. Eat not this flesh: Food avoidances in the Old World. Univ. Wisconsin Press, Madison.

192. Slevin, Joseph R. 1931. Log of the Schooner "Academy" on a voyage of scientific research to the Galápagos Islands. Calif. Acad. Sci. Occasional Papers. Vol. 17.

193. Sloane, Hans. 1709. A voyage to the islands Madera, Barbadoes, Nieves, S. Christophers and Jamaica. . . . London. 2 vols.

194. Smith, Malcolm A. 1931. Fauna of British India, Reptilia and Amphibia. London. Vol. 1.

195. Sparmann, André. 1787. Voyage au cap de Bon Espérance. Paris.

196. Spruce, Richard. 1908. Notes of a botanist on the Amazon and Andes, ed. and condensed by Alfred Russel Wallace. London.

197. Staunton, George. 1797. An account of an embassy from the King of Great Britain to the Emperor of China under Lord McCartney. London. 2 vols.

198. Stedman, John Gabriel. 1796. Narrative of a five years' experience against the revolted negroes of Surinam, in Guiana, on the wild coast of South America, from the year 1772 to 1776. . . . London. 2 vols.

199. Stephens, John Lloyd. 1843. Incidents of travel in Yucatán. London. 2 vols.

200. Stokes, John Lort. 1846. Discoveries in Australia, with an account of the coasts and rivers explored and surveyed during the voyage of the H.M.S. "Beagle," 1837-43. London. 2 vols.

201. Suzanne, Alfred. 1904. La cuisine et pâtisserie anglaise et américaine. Paris.

202. Tandy, William. 1833. Description of the Burmese Empire. Rome.

203. Theobald, W. 1870. Catalogue of the reptiles of British Burma, embracing the provinces of Pegu, Martaban and Tenasserim. J. Linn. Soc. (Zoology) 10:4-68.

204. Thompson, C. Wyville. 1877. The voyage of the "Challenger." London. Vol. 2.

205. Thompson, Ernest F. 1945. The fisheries of the Cayman Islands. Bull. Development and Welfare in West Indies 22:1:33.

206. Thompson, J. 1875. The straits of Malacca, Indo-China, and China; or ten years' travels, adventures, and residence aboard. New York.

206a. Thompson, J. Eric (ed.). 1958. Thomas Gage's travels in the New World. Univ. Oklahoma Press, Norman.

207. Thompson, Virginia. 1941. Thailand, the new Siam. New York.

208. The Times (London). November 13, 16, 1883.

120

209. Townsend, Charles Haskins. 1925. The Galápagos tortoises in their relation to the whaling industry. Zoologica 4(3): 55-135.

210. ———. 1926. The U.S.S. "Albatross" in Lower California seas. Amer. Mus. Nat. Hist. New York.

211. Travis, William. 1959. Beyond the reefs. New York.

212. Tressler, Donald K. 1923. The marine products of commerce. New York.

213. United Kingdom. 1952-53. Colonial Development Corporation. Reports and Accounts. London.

214. United States. 1861. Senate Executive Documents, No. 10. 36 Congress, 2d Session. Washington.

215. ———. 1954. Fish and Wildlife Service. Gulf of Mexico, its origins, waters and marine life. Fisheries Bull. No. 89. Washington.

216. ———. 1957. Trust Territory of the Pacific Islands. Notes on the present regulations and practices of harvesting sea turtle and sea turtle eggs in the Trust Territory of the Pacific Islands. Anthropological Working Paper no. 1, Office of the Staff Anthropologist. Agana, Guam (processed).

217. Uring, Captain Nathaniel. 1928. The voyages and travels of Captain Nathaniel Uring [1726]. The Seafarers' Library, London.

218. Vaillant, Leon and Guillaume Grandidier. 1910. Histoire physique, naturelle et politique de Madagascar. Paris. Vol. 17.

219. Van Bemmelen, J. F. 1891. Een Reisje naar de Zuidkust van de preanger. De Gids (Amsterdam) 55:4:253-89.

220. Van Denburgh, John. 1922. The reptiles of western North America. Calif. Acad. Sci. Occasional Papers. San Francisco. Vol. 10, no. 2.

221. Vásquez de Espinosa, Antonio. 1942. Compendium and description of the West Indies [1628]. Smithsonian Misc. Coll., Washington. Vol. 102.

222. Venezuelan Embassy, Washington. 1958. Arrival of turtles is harvest time for fishermen. Venezuela Up-to-Date, February, 1958, p. 17.

223. Villaluz, Domiciano K. 1953. Fish farming in the Philippines. Manila.

224. Villiers, A. 1958. Tortues et crocodiles de l'Afrique noire française. Inst. Français d'Afrique Noire, Initiations Africaines XV. Dakar.

225. Von Hagen, Victor W. 1949. Ecuador and the Galápagos Islands. Univ. Oklahoma Press, Norman.

226. Walter, Richard. 1928. Anson's voyage round the world [1748]. London.

227. Wetmore, Alexander. 1957. The birds of Isla Coiba, Panama. Smithsonian Misc. Coll., Washington. Publ. 134, no. 9.

228. Wheatley, Paul. 1959. Geographical notes on some commodities involved in Sung maritime trade. J. Malayan Br. Roy. Asiatic Soc. (Singapore) 32(2):1-140.

229. Wheeler, J. G. 1953. Memorandum on Green Turtle [1948]. In 90: Appendix 5, pp. 143-45.

230. Wied-Neuwied, Maximilian. 1820. Travels in Brazil in 1815, 1816 and 1817. London.

230a. Wiens, Herold J. 1962. Atoll environment and ecology. Yale Univ. Press, New Haven.

231. Wilbert, Johannes. 1955. Problematica de algunos metodos

< >
de pesca de los indios suramericana. Mem. Soc. Ciéncias Nat. "La Salle" (Caracas) 15:114-32.

232. Wilkes, Charles. 1850. Narrative of the United States Exploring Expedition. . . . Philadelphia. 3 vols.

233. Wilkinson, Henry C. 1950. Bermuda in the Old Empire. London.

234. ———. 1958. The adventurer of Bermuda. 2nd ed. London.

235. Williams, M. Woodbridge and Karl W. Kenyon. 1950. The turtle hunters of Scammon's Lagoon. Pacific Discovery (San Francisco) 3(4):4-16.

236. Wissowa, Georg (ed.). 1921. Pauly's Real-Encyclopädie der Klassischen Altertumswissenschaft. Stuttgart. 2nd ser., vol. 2A-1, pp. 427-33 ("Schildkrote").

237. Woodbury, George. 1954. The great days of piracy. London.

238. Young, Thomas. 1842. Narrative of a residence on the Mosquito Shore during the years 1839, 1840 and 1841. London.

239. Yonge, C. M. 1930. A year on the Great Barrier Reef. London.

240. Zuloaga, Guillermo. 1955. The Isla Aves story. Geogr. Rev. 45:172-78.

125

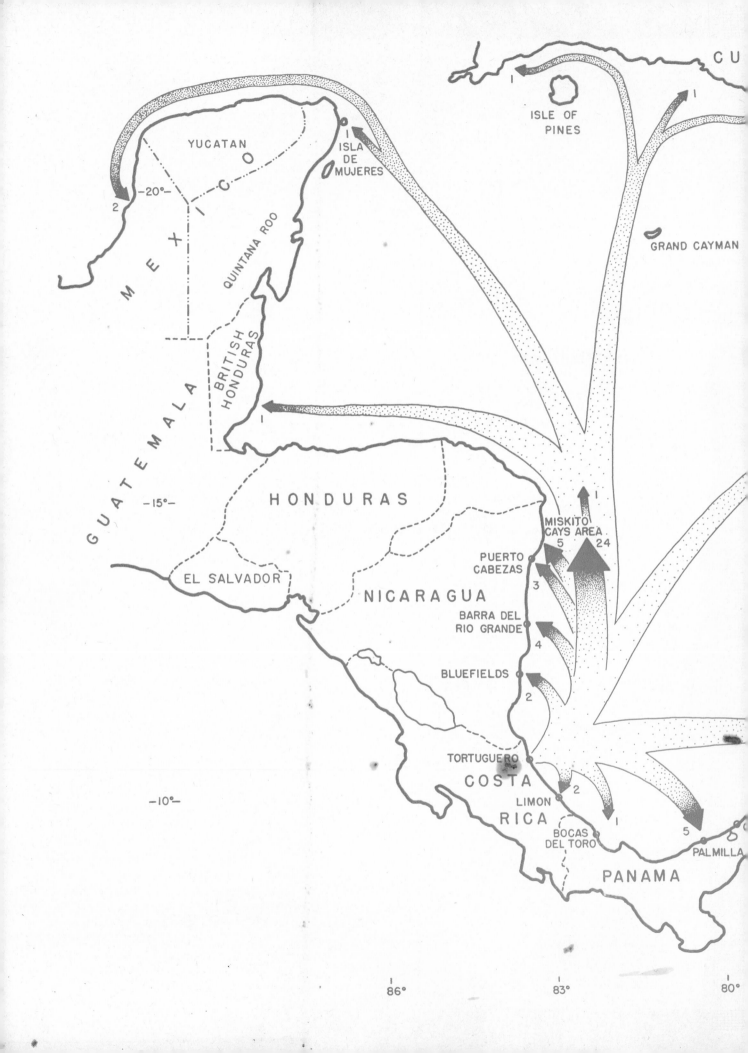